VIETNAM DOCTOR
The Story of Project Concern

VIETNAM DOCTOR

The Story of Project Concern

***

DR. JAMES W. TURPIN

with Al Hirshberg

McGRAW-HILL BOOK COMPANY

New York   Toronto   London   Sydney

To Mollie,
who showed me love and patiently waited
until I began to understand

Any man's death diminishes me, because I am involved in mankind.

JOHN DONNE

1624

VIETNAM DOCTOR
The Story of Project Concern

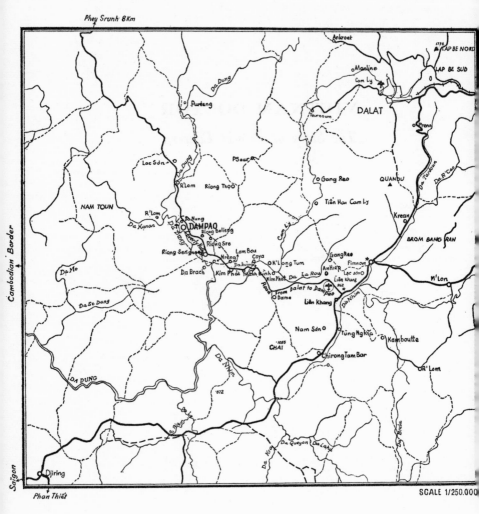

DaMpao and vicinity

CHAPTER

1

September mornings in DaMpao begin in a rosy light brightened by the night rains. From Project Concern's hilltop hospital you can see as well as feel the warm dampness that clings to everything. At six o'clock there is a fresh fragrance in the air, an exhilarating bonus for rising early. The valley below gleams with sparkling dew hanging like diamonds from pine, palm, and mahogany trees, from pineapple plants, and from banana trees that grow in the lush earth which fills abandoned foxholes. Water buffalo wallow in rice fields flat and wide enough to form a swampy moat discouraging to roving bands of Viet Cong. We call the place Loverly Valley, for the scene from the hill is breath-taking.

Below us on the opposite side from the valley runs a stream of clear, blue-green water that belies its ugly name —the Dung River. Its pace quickens in the early morning, adding to the glory of the surroundings. Adding more still are the sounds of the distant jungle, the high-pitched squawking of exotic birds, the deep-throated grunting of boars, the shrill chatter of gibbons, the raucous barking of wild dogs—dissonant noises that blend into a strangely harmonious chorus.

DaMpao lies at the southern terminus of the Ho Chi Minh Trail in the central highlands of South Vietnam, perhaps a hundred seventy-five miles northeast of Saigon and only a short distance from the Cambodian border. It is in Tuyen Duc province, its people divided between Vietnamese and Montagnard, with more of the latter. It doesn't matter. They are equally poor, equally hungry, equally sick of the war, equally in desperate need of medical attention.

One morning in September, 1964, I awoke on the dot of six and spent a luxurious moment or two between the damp sheets of my oversized army cot, contemplating the world through my cocoon of mosquito netting. My three roommates, all of different nationalities, were already stirring in the morning sun that streamed through windows whose gently flapping shutters had, as usual, blown open during the night.

There was Frank Hooper, our Canadian lab technician from Vancouver, British Columbia, who had joined us in Hong Kong on our arrival there in 1962, and never left. There was Guy Brehon, our camp manager, a transplanted Frenchman whom I had met through the Junior Chamber of Commerce in Orange, New South Wales, Australia. And there was Guy's Vietnamese assistant, Junior Duong.

We occupied one of several sleeping rooms of an H-shaped building. Ann Kidder and Lynn Allen, our American nurses, had another room. Ann was from Naperville, Illinois, Lynn from New York City. In a third room were Larry Wiesner, Roger Lee, and a young orphan boy from DaLat named Ha. DaLat, the capital of Tuyen Duc province, is about fifty kilometers northeast of DaMpao. Larry, who had had to leave the American Special Forces when he suffered a serious hearing loss, was with the Agency for International Development, popularly known as AID. He came from Florida. Roger, a Saigon Chinese, was my secretary. He had been brought in by a Japanese-American Special Forces sergeant, who asked us to care for him temporarily.

Our building was in a cluster of three at the rocky crest of the hill. Just below us was the hospital, a long, narrow structure with eighteen beds (since increased to thirty-five), and beside that a smaller building containing the dining room, kitchen, and quarters for our Koho staff. The Kohos are a subtribe of the Montagnards. Ours were mostly trainees for Project Concern's Village Medical Officer program. After several months' instruction they would return to their native villages nearby and set up clinics, as some of their V.M.O. predecessors had before them.

On the other side of the hill from the hospital were army barracks accommodating about a hundred security troops supplied by Lieng Khong, district headquarters, on orders of the provincial chief, Colonel De. Armed with flares, .30-caliber light machine guns, 60-millimeter mortars, and Browning automatic rifles, they gave us as much protection from the Viet Cong as we needed. The whole complex, once an American Special Services camp, had been abandoned during the summer of 1963.

While my roommates hovered between wakefulness and sleep, I climbed out of bed and looked down toward Loverly Valley. Even at that hour both Koho and Vietnamese patients were beginning to arrive. Products of altogether different backgrounds and cultures, the contrasts between the two are never so marked as in the brightness of the dawn.

Montagnards are not Chinese but of Indonesian, Polynesian, and Malaysian extraction. They have round eyes, square jaws, and very dark skin. Shy and subdued, they silently trudged up the hill barefoot, the men clad in shirts and loincloths, the women in single garments wrapped around their waists and reaching almost to their ankles. Some were bare-breasted and carrying babies in hand-woven slings thrown over their shoulders. They spoke softly, if at all, and rarely smiled as they approached the hospital.

The Vietnamese are Orientals, with the slanting eyes and sallow skin of their Chinese forebears. Village people wear a pajama-like outfit with full pants and high collars. Except for a few who came barefoot, they walked in thongs or sandals, called "go-aheads." Most of the women wore a cloth band tightly wrapped around the head, sometimes with the hair worked into it. As I watched, I could hear them chattering in the singsong tones of their native tongue and see them grinning at each other. Although some walked, more arrived in rugged little Lambrettas, three-wheeled Italian-made motor scooters that fly over muddy, pock-marked dirt roads like racing cars on superhighways. As always, I marveled at the fantastic number of people these vehicles can carry. The Vietnamese are short, compact people, but it is still startling to see as many as a dozen stream out of one Lambretta. There is a tiny seat on each side of the driver and a covered cab behind him. Before leaving the window, I counted ten people disembarking from a Lambretta cab.

None of my roommates had moved in the few moments I had been up. I gently touched Frank's shoulder and hissed, "Hey, wake up! They're swarming in today."

He sat on the side of his cot and reached for a cigarette. "Sounds like another busy one," he said. "I wonder if K'Che made it through the night."

Like the rest of us Frank was troubled over a young meningitis patient we had been trying desperately to save.

"The night crew should be up in a few minutes," I said. "They'll let us know at breakfast."

4

I gathered up pan, soap, towel, and razor, and headed for the kitchen, where our chef, Monsieur Thom, and his three assistants, a Vietnamese, a Montagnard, and a Cambodian refugee, had already been working an hour getting breakfast ready.

"*Bon jour,*" I said, using up one-sixth of my French vocabulary. Then I turned to K'Le, the Montagnard, and said, "*Niem sah.*" It means "Good body."

K'Le's eyes brightened in appreciation to be included in the morning greeting. There was nothing unusual about it, because I included him every day, but he always seemed pleasantly surprised.

"*Niem sah,* Bac-Si," he said, smiling.

"Bac-Si-Hakkah," which the people of the area have called me since we first set up Project Concern's hospital at DaMpao, is Koho for "the doctor who remembers."

I had breakfast of rice, toast, and hot chocolate. I prefer coffee in the morning, but the strong, acrid French coffee that was Monsieur Thom's specialty was more than I could take. As we ate, I learned that K'Che had held his own during the night, and there was hope he might pull through. After breakfast I got some hot water from a huge pot on the stove and went out on the porch to shave.

Just as I was wiping the last of the lather from my face, Ann Kidder came by and said, "Jim, we've got an emergency."

"What is it, Ann?" I asked as we hurried to the hospital.

"A newborn baby girl," she replied. "I think she has tetanus."

"And I think you ought to get some sleep," I said. "You've been on duty most of the night."

"I'll sleep after you've seen the baby."

The V.M.O. trainees and medical aides were already passing breakfast trays and morning medication when we reached the hospital. K'Moung, my chief medical assistant and Koho interpreter, was the first to greet me.

"Bac-Si," he said, leading me to the emergency room, "the father is a chief from Darkow. He says the baby, K'Sre, was born twelve days ago in his hut. The sorcerer cut the cord with a piece of dirty bamboo."

It wasn't the first time I had heard about sorcerers, nor would it be the last. I knew what had happened, for it was happening all the time. The father had let four precious days pass after the first serious symptoms appeared—four days of animal sacrifices, of incantations, of assurances that the evil spirits which had seized the child could be driven away. When they didn't disappear, there was the supreme effort on the fourth day—water buffalo entrails opened atop the village prayer pole, accompanied by more incantations. When that had no effect, the frantic chief insisted on taking the baby to the Western doctor on the hill at DaMpao. And I knew what would happen if the baby died. Naturally, it would be the Western doctor's fault. Ask the sorcerer.

In the arms of the young chief from Darkow was the contorted figure of an emaciated female infant, her face drawn up in a silent scream, her skinny arms and legs tensely flexed. Her father, deeply moved, talked rapidly, then K'Moung turned and said, "She won't eat, Bac-Si. She doesn't cry. She hardly moves. He is afraid she will die now because evil things have grasped her."

A quick examination proved both Ann and the chief right. The baby had tetanus and was near death.

"Ask Lynn to bring some vials of tetanus antiserum from the refrigerator, Ann," I said. "Then go to bed."

"If Darkow had a V.M.O., he'd have kept this from happening," she commented.

"But Darkow hasn't a V.M.O.," I said. "Perhaps if we save K'Sre the chief will send somebody."

We gave K'Sre heroic doses of antiserum and started her on intravenous feedings of sugar and water. We would not let her father touch her for fear the least stimulation might bring renewed and more severe contractions. By noon, after a bit of barbiturate sedation, there seemed to be some slight relaxation, and for the first time I began thinking K'Sre might have a chance.

The hospital was full of critically ill that morning. K'Che, our meningitis patient, was barely holding his own. He had developed pneumonia and was in a coma when his family had brought him in six days before. With catheter, I.V. (intravenous) fluids, antibiotics, and suctioning, the slender undernourished, bright-eyed ten-year-old Montagnard boy required constant attention. His entire family—parents, grandparents, and several brothers and sisters—stayed with him. They slept on the floor on mats and cloths, and we just worked around them. This is the only way you can conduct a hospital in the Orient. Either you let the whole family in and have a busy patient load or you bar the family and don't see anybody. If the relatives can't stay, the patient won't. And if the patient is too sick to decide for himself, the relatives won't let him stay without them.

We had a young Vietnamese mother who had been in mild shock from acute blood loss when her husband brought her in two days before. She had delivered a son at home, but the afterbirth hadn't come away. One of the older family members had acted as midwife, and when the mother continued to bleed she had called in a sorcerer. He had come reluctantly, for sorcerers, although willing to work with newborn babies, usually stay away from childbirth. A day of incantations resulted in no improvement, so the woman's husband brought her to us. Naturally, the baby came, too.

In the absence of a blood bank, we gave the mother some fluid called Dextran, a synthetic plasma volume expander. It tends to raise the blood pressure to nonshock levels, and in this case it worked. When I saw her that morning the woman was sitting up nursing her baby. The smiles on her face and on her husband's were worth the price of admission.

The prognosis wasn't so good for a badly dehydrated

Koho soldier from Phey Srung, a Special Forces camp in the mountains north of DaMpao. He had been brought in the day before with massive diarrhea of cholera in a Special Forces truck that came by three times a week with supplies for us. His wife and child were with him, but I couldn't give her much encouragement. We had him on I.V. feedings and chloramphenicol, but he had lost a terrible amount of body fluids and his condition was very poor when I saw him. He died the next night.

There were so many ward patients that morning rounds lasted longer than usual. Just as I was finishing them, a white Thai refugee boy from Hanoi was brought in hideously puffed up with water that his diseased kidneys could not eliminate. His face was so swollen that his eyes were shut. The child, who was nine, had nephritis—both kidneys infected—which seems to be almost an occupational disease of Thai refugees in the central highlands. The infection usually starts with a strep throat and spreads to the kidneys. It might also go to the heart and cause rheumatic heart disease.

"How long has he been sick?" I asked the father, through K'Moung.

"Many sore throats," was the answer.

"How many and how long?"

"Long time."

"What treatment?"

"Only the sorcerers."

We put the boy to bed and began draining the water off chemically with a drug called Diamox. His father, who had come alone, settled in for a long wait. Actually, it turned out to be two weeks before he could take the youngster home. We gave the child prophylactic antibiotics to cut down the chance of further strep infections, put him on a low-salt diet, kept him on diuretics, made him stay in bed, and had him on a very nutritious diet. He pulled through that time, but his father understood right from the beginning that his son couldn't live to become an adult because the kidneys were so badly infected.

We were so tied up with our critically ill bed patients that we didn't get the clinic started until ten o'clock, an hour later than usual. We had a big case-load there, too—one hundred and ten patients—with the result that nearly half the afternoon was gone before we finished lunch. We had intended to go to Psourr for the village clinic, but that was seven kilometers away, too far for safety at that hour. Seven kilometers doesn't sound like much, but on the rutty, dusty lanes that pass for roads it was an hour from DaMpao. That meant we couldn't get back before nightfall. If there were Viet Cong in the area, they would come out like locusts after the sun went down.

Our only protection when traveling was our British Land Rover, the Mollie T., named after my wife. White with red crosses, showing that Project Concern was an international relief agency, it was easy to see and generally respected in daylight but after dark little more than a slowly moving target for trigger-happy snipers. Instead of Psourr, I started out with Lynn Allen and five of our V.M.O. trainees for DaBrach, across the river and about half a mile from the hospital.

It may seem odd that we visited a place so close by, but we did this regularly because we found many people within walking distance who had not yet been motivated to come to us. Still heavily under the influence of the sorcerers, they were willing to see us in their own villages but not in our compound. Some, so terribly sick they had to be brought by relatives, belonged in the hospital, and occasionally would consent to go there. Most, however, came only as far as the village clinic. Even that was better than not coming at all.

As we came abreast of our own security forces on the hill I noticed there were more guards than usual on duty. I stopped when one held up his hand.

9

"Don't go too far, Bac-Si," he said. "The Viet Cong are out."

"In daylight?"

He nodded, and asked where we were headed.

"DaBrach," I said.

"No farther," he said. "And don't stay too long."

"Perhaps you'd better not go, Lynn," I said.

"You're going, aren't you?" she asked.

"Yes."

"Then I'll go," she said.

By driving as fast as I dared, I made DaBrach in fifteen minutes. There weren't many patients and we were through in an hour. On the way back to DaMpao we heard shots in the distance, hardly a phenomenon at night although it rarely happened during the day. The guard who had stopped us on the way out was obviously glad to see us back, and he waved us through with a smile.

At the hospital I asked Larry Wiesner, combat-trained and in charge of our reserve defenses, if he had heard anything.

"No more than usual," he said. "Everyone is a bit restless. We may have a little activity tonight."

"An alert?"

"Maybe."

"I'm glad Mollie took the children out of here."

"It was a good move," Larry said.

Especially, I thought, on nights such as this promised to be. Much as I missed the family, I was relieved when they left for Hong Kong and the States two weeks before. We were pretty safe on our hill, but you never knew what a stray shot aimed in that general direction might hit.

There was little dinner-table talk that night. Everyone was jumpy, and the Koho V.M.O.'s particularly so. They came from surrounding villages, and all the news that sifted through the local grapevine reached them. It was disquieting that night. Apparently, the whole area was crawling with Viet Cong.

Monsieur Tom had prepared a good dinner. Guy Brehon had gone to DaLat to market that morning and brought back some fish. We also had cabbage and some of Monsieur Tom's delicious egg custard, which more than made up for his horrible coffee. I even drank a little of that, just to be sociable.

Afterward Larry quietly went around checking our security. We all knew what to do in case of an alert, for we had had them before. The first thing was to turn off the generator so the lights would go out. This had no effect on the camp refrigeration, which was run by kerosene, and we had no electrically-operated hospital equipment. Lynn, Ann, and Guy took the responsibility of passing out arms, consisting of carbines, ammunition, and a few hand grenades. The arsenal was in the room next to where the nurses slept.

I had put a good deal of thought into that arsenal. We didn't carry weapons into the villages, but I felt we were justified in having something with which to protect ourselves in case the Viet Cong actually came into our compound and tried to hurt us or our patients, or to confiscate our medicine. We doubted it would ever happen, but we had arms and man power to supplement the security force if necessary. If we ever reached that point, Larry, not I, was the boss, and everyone stood ready to take orders from him.

Except Frank Hooper. Not that Frank wouldn't have helped if asked, but neither Larry nor I ever asked him, for we both knew how he felt. He was a true pacifist, a lover of animals as well as human beings, a man who could not bring himself to harm any living thing. He didn't know how to fire a weapon and had no desire to learn. Every night after supper he took a walk or played with Chopper, our monkey, read a bit, and then retired. He followed this routine come hell or high water. Nothing, including an alert, could make him change it. I don't think even an actual Viet Cong invasion could have. Whenever there was an alert, the rest of us went into foxholes which Larry had had dug at each of the four corners atop the hill, but Frank acted as if nothing unusual were going on. If it came early, he kept on playing with Chopper or reading; if late, he went to bed and stayed there.

Each of us was assigned a specific foxhole, to which we went as soon as the alert came. We were expected to stay there until we had the all clear, but sometimes alerts lasted so long that we moved into an old mortar bunker adjoining the building. The longer the alert, the less the danger, for the Viet Cong depended heavily on surprise, which stopped being a factor the moment the alert began. The mortar bunker, big enough to accommodate all of us, was primarily for the use of the special forces, several of whom manned it during alerts. Besides the mortar circle there was a machine-gun pit commanding the field of fire in front of the hospital. Neither mortar nor machine gun had been used since we had been there, but they were kept in working order.

When Larry finished his check of our reserve defenses, he joined me in the sitting room. I was writing letters and, after stopping long enough to exchange a few words with him, I continued to do so. He picked up a book and began reading. Frank was in the big bedroom playing with Chopper. The girls had gone to their room on the other side of the building. There was a misty rain, so slight that it made no noise as it brushed the roof. Down in the dining room we could see the reflection of an old Laurel and Hardy movie, supplied by the U.S. Information Service. Offduty members of the security force and their families (relatives followed Koho soldiers wherever they went just as they followed their sick into hospitals) were crowded into the big room. Viet Cong or no Viet Cong, missing a movie was unthinkable.

As I wrote to Mollie, everything seemed unusually peaceful. The gentle rain, the sounds of laughter from the dining room, the still darkness of the night, the flickering lights from the hospital, even the shots off in the direction of the jungle all made the war and the Viet Cong seem very far away.

Suddenly the lights went out, and there was first a cry, then a series of screams from the dining room. Yelling children were scooped up by anxious mothers, doors were flung open, people poured out of the building, confused, shouting, stumbling, and running off in all directions. Half-uniformed soldiers snapped rifle bolts shut as they emerged from the dining room and thundered past us to their prepared defensive positions.

H'Klas and K'Crah, two of our medical aides, darted into the sitting room. They paused just long enough for H'Klas to pant, "Viet Cong come here tonight—soon!" Then they rushed off. Larry was already at the door before I was on my feet. I heard Ann and Lynn talking softly in the ammunition room and whispered voices directing the distribution of weapons we hoped and prayed would never be used. Somebody thrust a sub-machine gun into my arms and I hurried to my assigned fox hole, nearly stumbling over K'Moung.

"What's happening, Mr. K'Moung?" My breath was coming in such short gasps I could hardly get the words out.

"Viet Cong near to you," he said. "Want to come here, take our medicine. They come tonight!"

We ran together to the fox hole, then I slid into it beside K'Crah, who was already there. K'Moung's position was in a shallow trench directly behind us, and I could hear the rasp of his breath at my shoulder. Down near the hospital somebody was feeding an ammunition belt into the ready position of a .30-caliber machine gun. There were muffled orders and the scuffle of heavy boots. As I tried to peer through the mist, I saw something move, then heard the unfamiliar, frightening sound of rubber sandals on moist dirt.

"Mr. K'Moung, they're here!" I whispered.

"No, Bac-Si," he said softly. "They do not come now. But they come tonight."

My eyes and ears were playing tricks. It wasn't the first time. At every alert I always imagined the worst.

Two shots rang out in the direction of the hospital. Who had fired? Were we under attack? A Vietnamese lieutenant hurried by, obviously annoyed. A minute later the whole area was lit by a parachute flare. The sudden brilliant almost blinding light gave us a clear view of the entire compound. Except for the eerie whiteness from the flare, everything seemed normal. There were no strange faces, no hostile movements from any direction.

"A false alarm." I thought the words and unintentionally spoke them aloud.

"No, Bac-Si," K'Moung murmured. "They are down below. They come tonight."

He was half right. A heavy force of Viet Cong was concentrated around Filion, a village about twenty-five kilometers away. I don't know what their intentions were, but they were headed in our direction. Driven off before they reached DaMpao, they never got much closer, but they were a threat. That was the trouble—they were always a threat.

We were in the fox hole for three hours, then made our way back to the mortar bunker. Now it was after midnight, but the elert was still on. Monsieur Thom had made coffee, which Ann and Lynn were passing around the bunker. Sopping wet from the light but steady mist, I would have drunk mud if it were hot. Trying to ignore the taste, I took a gulp. It felt good going down. We kept our guns at the ready, and spoke in whispers. The alert was still on, as it would be for three more hours. We would not go to bed until the all clear came from the security forces below.

14

"Listen."

Ann, her green eyes shining behind the horn-rimmed glasses she wore, one arm raised in an arresting gesture, had a half-smile on her face. From the direction of the barracks we heard the softly swelling voices of Montagnard men and women as they sang in their native Koho tongue.

For a moment I thought Ann was calling our attention only to the fact of their singing. Then I recognized the melody, even though I could not understand the words.

"Onward, Christian soldiers . . ."

They sang for more than an hour, hymn after hymn, their voices rising from the dark of the night, the words strange but the music familiar as the gospel I had learned as a boy and once preached as a Methodist minister. They stopped only when the all clear came, at three in the morning. I went to bed, but not to sleep, for the hymns of my childhood, sung in Koho on a hill in the central highlands of South Vietnam, stayed with me all night. They seemed, somehow, to bring my whole life into focus, to make all I was trying to do worth while, even to ease the pain of longing for Mollie and our four children, none of whom I would see again for months.

CHAPTER

2

The two most vivid memories of my early childhood were medical experiences involving my grandfathers, who lived a mile from each other in the southeastern hills of Kentucky. Papa Duke, my mother's father—Dr. John Wesley Duke— was a country doctor. His house was in Hindman, his practice all over Knott County. Papa Turpin, my father's father —James Henry Turpin—was a lumber-mill operator. Papa Duke, a deeply religious Methodist, was a Kentuckian, born and bred in the heart of Appalachia. Papa Turpin came from Texas, where he had once been a horse wrangler. Both were short, lean, energetic men. At seventy-five, Papa Duke still had a full head of magnificent blond hair and sharp blue eyes that crinkled at the corners. He died some years ago, but Papa Turpin is ninety, and still active at this writing. He runs a small coal mine in Pineville, Kentucky.

My younger brother Bill and I were born and brought up in Ashland, Kentucky, where my father, James William Turpin, was a steel-mill foreman, but we spent our summers in Hindman. There, during the summer of 1937 when I was nine, I had those two unforgettable childhood experiences. The first occurred one afternoon when Papa Duke took me along to help him give shots to the children in a country school. Naturally, he didn't let me handle the needle, but he let me stand beside him as he spoke these words to thirty-seven girls and boys ranging in age from six to sixteen:

"Children, I helped to bury some of your aunts and uncles, even some of your older brothers and sisters because I didn't have what was needed to save their lives. Many of our people have died for lack of strong medicine to fight the tiny but powerful germs that got inside their bodies. I've brought that medicine with me today. My grandson here will grow strong because he has had the shots I am now going to give you. He's here to help me and to tell you it hurts only a little."

As the children lined up, the eldest first, the youngest last, Papa Duke let me prepare them for the shots by putting alcohol on their arms. I never forgot the glow of satisfaction that came from performing this simplest of medical chores. When it was all over, I walked out feeling I might have saved some child from a horrible disease, perhaps even death.

Later that summer Papa Turpin took Bill and me out log-

16

ging with one of his crews. Two or three of our uncles, including Pat, Dad's youngest brother, who was only a few years older than I, were in the party which consisted mostly of bearded mountain men who worked for Papa Turpin. As we made our way through the dense woods, Pat suddenly screamed. He had been bitten in the ankle by a black snake which one of the men split in two lengthwise with an ax even before Pat hit the ground.

Papa Turpin bent down, told Pat to bite into a piece of wood so that he could stand the pain, made two X-shaped incisions with his knife just above the tiny twin puncture holes on Pat's ankle, sucked hard on the incisions, and spat mouthfuls of blood and venom on the ground. When he was sure the poison was out, he calmly directed the men as they carefully carried Pat back through the woods to the house.

"Will he be all right, Papa?" Bill asked.

"I think so. We got everything out pretty fast. He'll have a swollen leg and high fever for a while, but he'll be okay."

While Papa Duke's lesson in preventive medicine and Papa Turpin's in first aid may not have been directly responsible for my own decision to become a doctor, they certainly helped set me on that path. Even so, I made it in a roundabout way, for other events first diverted me in the direction of the ministry.

There was my conversion at the age of twelve, when I gave my life to Christ during a Sunday service in our Methodist church in Ashland. There was my fling at preaching in 1942, when I was fourteen. There was my part-time Salvation Army service while I was stationed in Jacksonville, Florida, as a navy seaman second class in 1946. There was my vague idea of someday going to the Orient as a medical missionary. But the compelling reason for my entering the Methodist ministry had no relation to any of those religious experiences or notions. I turned to the church because, as a pre-med student at Emory University in Atlanta, I flunked organic chemistry and had nowhere else to go.

While this disaster wrecked my medical-school ambitions for the moment, it led me to the greatest break of my life. It forced me to go to summer school, and that was where I met my wife.

I first saw Martha Williamson on a hot June day in 1948 when she walked into a speech class two days late. One of the most beautiful girls I had ever seen, she was a brunette with deep, dark-brown eyes dressed in a pink pinafore with wide, lacy straps. She had the delicacy of a Dresden doll, but was not so delicate as she looked. Nineteen years old, she was a top-ranking woman tennis player in Georgia. She came by her talent honestly. Her father, Robert Lamar Williamson, a successful Atlanta businessman popularly known as Molly, was an outstanding tennis player, despite the fact that he weighed three hundred and fifty pounds. Robert Ripley once featured him in one of his "Believe It or Not" drawings as the "world's heavyweight tennis champion." Martha, whose nickname was also Mollie, was late for class because she had gone to Nashville with her parents to play in a tournament.

A junior at Agnes Scott, Mollie took the speech class at Emory only because she had nothing else to do that summer. On the day she came in for the first time I gave a talk called, "How to Make a Mountain out of a Molehill," which was my view on civil rights. I told how racial prejudice had been blown all out of proportion because of stories, especially in the South, of Negro men attacking white women. I said that the blood of the Negro was the same as the blood of the white person, and so was everything else except his rights.

When a mutual friend introduced me to Mollie after class she said, "Your talk on racial prejudice was good. May I have a copy of it?"

"You mean you liked it?"

"Very much."

"You're an Atlantan, aren't you?"

"Yes."

"And you still liked it?"

"Of course," she said. "I think the young people's group at my church would enjoy it, too. Will you give it there Sunday night?"

"Won't they resent a liberal view of race relations?" I asked.

"Why should they? They know what you say is true."

So I repeated the class talk before the church young people's group the following Sunday. By then Mollie and I discovered we had a number of things in common. We were both Methodists, deeply interested in the church. We had both toyed with the idea of becoming missionaries, but still weren't sure that that was what we wanted. We both loved sports. And it wasn't long before we loved each other. We were engaged by the end of the summer.

Our romance softened the blow of my not being able to get into medical school. My ambitions of becoming a doctor apparently had gone out the window with my organic-chemistry failure. I had hoped that by repeating the course that summer I could save the situation, but in July I learned that even if I passed there was no hope, at least not for 1948. There were too many people applying, including a huge wave of former GI's who, having taken accelerated under-graduate courses, were now ready for medical school. Nearly a thousand were trying to get into the one at Emory alone. Even though I did well in organic chemistry at summer school—I finally got a B—I threw away my medical-school application and decided to become a minister.

That fall Mollie returned to Agnes Scott wearing a diamond engagement ring that wasn't entirely paid for. I had once worked in a jewelry store in Ashland. The owner sent me the ring for a down payment, agreeing to accept the rest in installments which I would pay by selling blood at

19

twenty-five dollars a pint. I had worked in a ward and later as an operating-room technician at Emory Hospital. They were willing to buy my blood every six weeks instead of making me wait the normal period of two to three months.

I plunged into a frenetic routine that included football, a full study schedule, preaching at a Negro church outside the city, helping the Reverend Robert Kerr at College Park Methodist Church in suburban Atlanta, and peddling blood. I didn't have to do that to pay for the ring. My father would have been glad to help me. I didn't have to preach at one church and help the pastor at another. I didn't have to play football. I could have satisfied my obligations and lived a normally busy life simply by dividing my time between the classroom and College Park. Besides, I would have enjoyed spending more time with Bob Kerr, a Lincolnesque figure for whom I had deep admiration and affection. But as I look back on that mad, frantic year I realize what I was trying to prove. All the extra work kept me too busy to think about the disappointment of not getting into medical school, a blow far more crushing than I knew at the time it happened. And, since I was never absolutely sure the ministry was what I really wanted, I tried to get so deeply involved in it that I didn't have time to want anything else.

I married Mollie instead of attending commencement. The wedding, a big one that took place on my graduation day, June 4, 1949, was something of a social event, for the Williamsons were well known in Atlanta. Naturally, the ceremony was performed by Bob Kerr. After a honeymoon at Lake Trahlyta in north Georgia, we went to a Methodist summer retreat in North Carolina before returning to Atlanta. Our first home was an apartment in Gilbert Hall at Candler School of Theology on the Emory campus. We lived there for eight months before I was made student pastor of a little parsonage at Winter's Chapel, about twelve miles north of Atlanta. The appointment, called a student charge, was one of the few available to first-year theology men, and I was very fortunate to get it. With a beautiful bride, a new home, a parsonage of my own, and a good salary, I should have been supremely happy. Instead, although hardly miserable, I was a bundle of nerves.

Leaving the Emory campus meant giving up my last tie with the medical profession. Right up to the day we vacated Gilbert Hall, I continued to work as an operating-room technician at the hospital. It was a menial job, but it kept me in touch with work I loved. I renounced even that crumb of satisfaction when we went to Winter's Chapel, for now I had to devote all my time to my studies and work in the ministry. I had no enthusiasm for either. My sermons were uninspired, my interest in the spiritual problems of my church members meager, my hopes for the future dashed by the realization that I wasn't really fit for my calling.

In the early months of our marriage Mollie and I often talked of becoming missionaries. At fifteen she had had a religious experience similar to mine, in which she gave her life to Christ and promised to work in some way for the church. Because of these adolescent experiences we both felt an obligation which we hoped to satisfy by going overseas after I had completed my religious studies. Occasionally we met missionaries home on furlough, and one night had a chance to talk to a couple recently returned from Africa. I asked the man, a Methodist minister, how he liked it.

He told me he had found it very rewarding, then went into a lengthy description of his life there. The more he talked, the more we realized that he only worked with the natives but otherwise had nothing to do with them. I wanted to ask him if he felt the same about Negroes in Africa as he did in Atlanta, where he was brought up, but that wasn't necessary because he answered it himself.

"Naturally," he said, "we had nothing to do with these people socially, any more than we would here."

Later I asked Mollie what she thought of him. "Not much," she said. "He's not a real missionary. He's just play-acting. He looks down his nose at the very people he's supposed to help."

My dissatisfaction increased so much that Mollie began calling me "ye olde restless one." I could have found plenty to do in my own little parsonage, but it failed to hold my interest. Unable to sit still, I took up flying. I had wanted to fly in the Navy, but never got the opportunity. Now I spent a few hours a week at the airport, where my lessons were a welcome relief from classroom work that had become drudgery. I hated Greek, a major language in the theology curriculum, and barely managed to pass it. I had become a fairly good speaker, but now had to unlearn what I knew and start all over again. In preaching, it was necessary to master "projection" and "diaphragmatic breathing," neither of which I could understand, much less master. Worried, upset, disappointed, frustrated, and unhappy in my work, I began getting stomach pains. I thought they were caused by gastritis, but when they persisted I consulted a doctor. He found that I had a small ulcer.

Mollie was pregnant with Keith, our first child, who was born in December, 1950. She wasn't surprised when I told her the source of my stomach trouble. Although we had not talked much about my disappointment in having to settle for the ministry when I couldn't get into medical school, she knew as well as I that I was in the wrong profession. When she learned of my ulcer, she said, "Jim, you're literally eating your heart out over not being a doctor. Why don't you make another try for medical school?"

"I wish I could," I said. "But I have an obligation to the Methodist church. I can't just walk out on school, job, and everything."

"My obligation is as great as yours," she said. "Maybe we can satisfy it some other way. You could become a medical missionary, you know."

"I'd have to become a doctor first. I can't do that without going to medical school. And I can't even get in."

"How do you know? You've never tried."

She was quite right—I never had. After flunking organic chemistry I hadn't even applied for medical school because I felt it was hopeless. Perhaps it wasn't hopeless now. In summer school I had made up the failed course, and if they would count that B the second time around I might have a chance. I thought about it during the fall of 1950, but hesitated to make a move, partly because my conscience bothered me over the prospect of leaving the ministry, but mostly because I was afraid of being turned down.

When I told Mollie of my fears, she said, "Oh, Jim, that's ridiculous. When you worked at the hospital, the doctors and everyone else were so fond of you. All they had to do was look at you to know what kind of doctor you'd be. There's more to the medical profession than a record on paper. There's your attitude and aptitude and the intensity of your desire. This will all come out in interviews and will more than make up for an old flunking mark that you've already erased."

Still I hesitated. Then one day, as I was crossing the Emory campus, I ran into Harrison Reeves, a third-year medical student whom I had known as an undergraduate. It was the first time I had seen him in a couple of years. We shook hands, and he asked me how things were going.

"So-so," I said. "How about you?"

"Wonderful," he said. "Med school is great. I can't wait to finish."

"I wish I were in your shoes," I said. "I couldn't make it."

"You're not happy in the ministry?"

"I'd rather be a doctor."

"Then, for heaven's sake, apply for med school."

"I can't get in. I once flunked organic chemistry. I made it up later, but what good will that ever do me?"

"Listen, Jim," Harrison said, "there are plenty of guys in

23

med school with bad marks on their undergraduate record that they never made up. Feeling as you do, you're an idiot if you don't apply."

I decided to see if a surgeon who had encouraged me when I worked in the hospital might help me, but I couldn't remember his name. I checked the list of staff doctors at the hospital.

"Abbott, Anderson, Bartholomew, Brown—" I stopped. Brown—Robert Brown—that was it. I telephoned his office, told his secretary why I wanted to see him, and made an appointment. When I arrived, I spent anxious moments wondering if he would remember me, before the secretary announced, "Dr. Brown will see you now, Mr. Turpin."

I walked in on a tall, gray-haired, distinguished man in a long white coat and realized, to my dismay, that I had never seen him before in my life. I was about to stammer an apology when he invited me to sit down, then said, "My secretary tells me you want to go to medical school."

"Yes," I said.

"I know more about you than you think," the doctor said. "My father is a Methodist minister. So are you. I understand you want to be a medical missionary. It's a fine idea. Now, you'll need a good letter of recommendation, which I'll be delighted to provide. You see, I'm on the admissions committee. That might help some."

We talked a few minutes before I walked out in a rosy haze. Not until I reached home that night did I recall the name of the doctor I had meant to see. It was Martin, not Brown.

In the next few months I filled out applications, submitted to interviews, and had lengthy talks, not only with Mollie but with Dean William Cannon, who had advised me on my theology-school curriculum. He agreed that if I could get into medical school that was where I belonged, and he assured me that if I failed to make it I could stay at Winter's Chapel as long as I remained a theology student.

He also helped to ease my conscience, for I felt my obligation to the ministry as keenly as ever and was disturbed over the possibility of abandoning it.

"Medicine is a noble profession," he said. "To leave the ministry for that is no disgrace."

When I walked into the house at Winter's Chapel one spring day, Mollie handed me a long white envelope that had arrived in the mail. We sat together on the living-room divan while I ripped it open. The first sentence of the letter inside began: "We are pleased to inform you that your application—"

"Darling, you're in!" Mollie cried.

My medical career was about to begin.

CHAPTER

3

I entered medical school with mixed emotions, happy to have been accepted, conscience-stricken to be leaving the ministry. It was a conflict which would take years and much soul-searching to resolve. Mollie and I had promised to give our lives to the church, and now we were leaving it. We had been taught to believe not simply that this was wrong, but that it carried a taint of disgrace. At least I planned to become a medical missionary. That gave us plenty of room to rationalize.

We moved in with Mollie's mother, now a widow working as a secretary in the Georgia Tech athletic office. Mollie, who had taught school until Keith was born, went back to teaching to help support the family. From an economic standpoint, I was a dead loss. My medical-school expenses, which were considerable, would have to be taken care of by loans and whatever Mollie and Mrs. Williamson could spare. I had no time for anything but my studies.

My only other interest besides the family was the church. Mollie and I, motivated partly by conscience and partly by sincere desire, became very active at St. Mark's Church, where she had gone as a girl. We formed a Sunday-school class called the Christian Forum, which we hoped to make truly ecumenical. From time to time we brought in Jewish and Catholic spiritual leaders, but when we wanted to invite a Negro the parishioners raised such a fuss the idea was abandoned. While we found this ridiculous and frustrating, we managed, at least, to start a good Sunday school, and the Christian Forum is still in existence at St. Mark's.

I hadn't been in medical school two months before I ran into another type of conflict, this time between science and the church. I had a young anatomy instructor who had just come over from Ireland. He met us in groups of six for classes which were held whenever the spirit moved him. We gave him our home telephone numbers so that he could call us at any time. He scheduled an autopsy at the last minute on a Sunday morning, but he couldn't get an answer at our house because we were all in church. He kept calling for the three hours we were away, and when he finally got me he was fit to be tied.

"Where were you?" he demanded.

"In church," I said.

"Damn church!" he snapped. "You're a medical student and you're supposed to be available when we want you."

He told me to get down there as fast as I could, and when I arrived—about an hour after everyone else—he gave me another dressing down.

"Church or no church," he said, "in this business you're always on call. Don't ever forget that."

Not until later did I realize I had already become more student than minister. I should have been shocked by the instructor's blasphemy. Instead, I felt like a kid caught playing hooky. I knew I wouldn't change my routine on the chance that he might spring another Sunday-morning class someday, for church attendance was too important to me. On the other hand, I understood for the first time that a medical student's time is never his own, any more than a doctor's. Therefore, I reasoned, my not being available was worse than the instructor's lack of respect. This in itself was a jolt. I never thought I would find an excuse for anyone to damn the church.

Part of the regular second-year curriculum included a psychiatry class which met for three hours one morning a week. The class actually was a session in analysis, with the professor the doctor and one of the twelve students the patient. It was a rather weird experience, for nobody knew who the patient would be. The technique was to wait until somebody said something. The pressure would build up for thirty or forty minutes until finally one of us felt he had to speak and would say whatever was on his mind. Then the professor encouraged the rest of us to act as therapists.

Everyone has a sore spot, something that may have been bothering him for years. Mine was my church problem, which really dated all the way back to my conversion at the age of twelve. The whole class knew about my theological background, that I had been a preacher, that I had had a congregation of my own, and that I intended to become a medical missionary. Some resented this, for, without meaning to, I must have given the impression of supreme egotism. I had something they didn't have, for I was a devoted, dedicated Christian who would introduce Western medicine to Timbuctoo or some equally remote part of the world. But they suspected the depth of my dedication was not what it appeared to be, that it wasn't as genuine as it looked, that I really didn't want to become a medical missionary at all.

I knew nothing of this feeling about me among my classmates until the day it was my turn to be the "patient." By then half a dozen others had been through the mill. I knew it would happen to me sooner or later, and I hardly looked forward to the experience. During one of those long, oppressive silent periods I had the uncomfortable feeling that everyone expected me to speak. It seemed almost as though I knew I needed help and this was the day I would get it.

I cleared my throat and said something like, "I grew up with certain beliefs. They were inherited beliefs, so I accepted them as my own. Now I'm not sure I have properly reinterpreted them. Perhaps they really aren't my own. Perhaps I simply fell heir to them without fully accepting them."

The more I talked the better I felt, for this was a sensitive subject which I had never openly expressed before, even to Mollie. There was no question that I had doubts, not about my faith but about where I belonged within its framework. I didn't blurt everything out that day in the classroom; in fact, the professor discouraged us from that. All he wanted us to do was talk enough about our problem to enable the others, the "therapists," to ask pertinent questions. It was in these questions that I learned that they thought I had a smug feeling of superiority because of my background and that they wondered if I really did plan to become a medical missionary.

Before I was through that day I wondered myself. Up to then I had accepted the possibility as a suitable substitute for the ministry I had renounced. This, in itself, was an expression of weakness in the eyes of my classmates. They wanted to know if I really looked forward to life as a medical missionary or if I were using it as a sop to my conscience. It was a delicate question which would require plenty of thought before an answer could be found, but at least now it was out in the open. I felt better when the day's session was over, for I had at last faced up to a problem that had been with me from the day of my conversion.

I did not immediately give up the idea of becoming a

medical missionary. I simply no longer took as a matter of course that this would be my way of life. Mollie and I would have many talks before finding the answer. This had nothing to do with our faith, which was as strong as ever. At no time did I doubt the teachings of my church—only where I belonged within its framework.

During my medical school career we inquired about medical missionary work a number of times. We were twice interviewed by Mr. M. O. Williams, a field director of the Methodist Board of Missions and Church Extension. Once we drove to Nashville to be interviewed by a Methodist missionary regional board. We were tentatively accepted as missionaries-to-be after my graduation from medical school, but this was not a commitment. Until we actually reached that point we could turn the appointment down or the board could turn us down. We simply made a loose agreement, subject to further consideration, to go into the work when the time came, in which case we would go wherever the board sent us.

In my junior year at medical school Bishop Arthur Moore of the North Georgia and South Georgia Methodist Conference ordained me as a church deacon in a special service at the Wesley Methodist Church in Atlanta. I invited all my classmates to this ceremony, but only one came. I think the others stayed away purposely, perhaps because they knew my intentions better than I did myself.

During my junior and senior years I changed my mind a dozen times about what I wanted to be. For a while I thought I would specialize in obstetrics. Then I thought about becoming an ophthalmologist. One month I considered medical missionary work, the next general practice. Not until a few months before receiving my medical degree did I know my next step. By then we had two little boys—Payton was born in August, 1952—and were up to our ears in debt.

"How can we leave the country owing so much to so many people?" Mollie and I asked each other.

So again we stifled our consciences and turned away from church work. After notifying the Methodist missionary board that we had decided not to take an appointment, I accepted an internship at the Crawford Long Memorial Hospital in Atlanta. We moved out of Mrs. Williamson's house into an apartment provided by the hospital and settled down for a year of hard work and more soul-searching.

For, even as I drifted away from a missionary career, things happened that constantly reminded me of it. At the hospital my dual status as a doctor and a minister was well known, and I soon found myself being called upon to act in both capacities. Often a dying patient requested spiritual aid, or the family of one who had just passed away needed someone to lead them in prayer. If it occurred at an odd hour I was usually the only clergyman available.

While perfectly willing to help anyone I could, I far preferred giving medical assistance, and would have confined my activities exclusively to that if I could have done so in good conscience. My conscience troubled me enough without these repeated reminders of the profession I had left. So did Mollie's.

"Darlin'," I told her one night near the end of the Crawford Long internship in 1956, "I'm still not sure what to do."

"I'll accept any decision you make," she said.

"That will be fine as long as you don't tell me to let my conscience be my guide," I said.

"I was just about to," she said.

I took a residency at the Sonoma County Hospital in Santa Rosa, California, where I spent a year bridging the gap which every doctor faces between the academic environment and the outside world of practical medicine. As usual, Mollie taught school to help keep our financial troubles from getting worse. We both fell in love with

California but, since all our family ties were in the East, had no intention of staying there beyond my hospital residency.

Besides enjoying Santa Rosa, I learned some of the nuances of my profession. Jack Dunn, the chief resident in surgery, although my age, had a richer medical background because he had started well ahead of me. One day he taught me a lesson I never forgot. A nurse had called me into the emergency room with a puzzling patient, an attractive woman of twenty-five who seemed to have nothing wrong with her but was totally unresponsive. Her breathing was regular, her blood pressure and pulse normal, and there were no unusual odors. Yet she didn't react at all to pinprick or other stimulation. I tested and retested her without any change, and was just about to call Jack when he walked in.

"Trouble?" he asked.

"I'm afraid so," I said. Then I told him of my findings and the patient's negative reactions. As I talked he laid a hand on her abdomen, and before I was through he had an answer.

"Well," he said, "that's California for you."

"What do you mean, Jack?"

"She's having an acute anxiety reaction."

"From what?"

He shrugged. "Who knows? Fed up with her family maybe. Perhaps her husband doesn't pay enough attention to her and this is her way of getting it. Anyhow, she's a hypochondriac. We have dozens of patients like that, mostly women. It must be the air out here or something."

"What's the treatment?"

"Sedation and rest," Jack said. "And when she goes home, a lot more affection than she's been getting."

Never having seen anything like that before, I could hardly believe my ears. Yet, sure enough, Jack was quite right. After a couple of days of complete rest the patient was fine. Before I left Sonoma I must have seen twenty such cases.

31

One of our best friends that year was a young doctor named Jim Mushovic, who was about to take over a practice in Coronado. Whenever we talked of our future plans, Jim described the place as a little bit of heaven. A small city across the harbor from San Diego and only a few miles from the Mexican border, it was, he told us, a community of prosperous people who basked in the sun in balmy weather that rarely changed. The beach was one of the best in California, the people among the friendliest. Jim couldn't wait to get there.

"I envy Jim," I told Mollie one day. "He's got such a wonderful spot to go to."

"I know," she said.

"I wish we could go somewhere like that."

"So do I."

"But we can't," I said.

"No," she agreed, "we can't."

We couldn't for two reasons. One was our family ties. The other was an almost nagging conviction that if we didn't do missionary work we should find a rural area in the southeastern part of the country where we were needed. What we didn't admit, either to ourselves or each other, was that we were having too good a time in California, especially for a couple of people who only two years before had talked grandly about doing something for the underprivileged in some remote corner of the world.

A month before my year of residency at Sonoma ended I flew back to Atlanta and talked with a doctor in Chamblee, Georgia, not far from Winter's Chapel. His was a rural practice, and he told me there were plenty of places in Georgia that needed dedicated doctors. I heard about an opening in Chickamauga, a small mill town with a rich Civil War tradition in the northwest corner of the state. I drove there with Mrs. Williamson one day and, while I hardly found it the ideal place to live, it didn't seem too bad and it certainly needed a general practitioner. After a consultation with Dr. Fred Simonton, then vice-president of the American Academy of General Practice, I decided to go there.

Mollie was expecting Scott, our third son, when we arrived in early July, 1957. We got there on a day so hot that every move was an effort, and by the time I had unloaded the car I was exhausted. I collapsed in a chair on the porch, hoping the intense heat and oppressive humidity were unusual, but strongly suspecting they weren't. These suspicions were confirmed in the days that followed, for Chickamauga at that time of the year was a steamy oven. Mollie and I had no trouble pretending we were in Africa.

The town was stifling in more ways than one. Its educational system was poor, its social life limited. We made some friends with whom we enjoyed getting together when we had time, but almost every white person in town had typically reactionary feelings about Negroes, which we found annoying. After a while Mollie asked when I came home, "How many times did you hear the word 'nigger' today?" And I would reply, "Six, eight, ten, twelve—" or whatever the figure, then ask her. We kept count of this dreary statistic for months. Worse than the sound of the word, which grated on our nerves like a long fingernail scratching across a pane of glass, was the fact that there seemed to be nothing we could do to eliminate it from the local vocabulary. Whenever I tried, I was met by the cold stares of people who had been friendly only seconds before.

The hated word certainly helped to drive us out of Chickamauga, especially when Keith and Pate began bringing it home from school. When children at the first- and second-grade level were referring to Negroes as "dirty niggers" despite all our efforts to stop them, it was time to think of moving. I'm sure it wasn't easy for the boys to understand why we forbade them to use a term they heard from adults as well as other children wherever they went.

Unlike profanity, it was accepted in the nicest homes in Chickamauga.

One Sunday I was invited to preach as guest minister at the local Methodist church. Choosing as my subject "The Brotherhood of Man—the Fatherhood of God," I made an open plea for racial equality. The sermon was greeted by stony silence from almost everyone except Mollie, who thought it was one of my better efforts. The minister never again asked me to preach.

Sticky as the hot summer was, I think I would have swapped it for the penetrating cold that came in the late fall and early winter. By then I not only had office hours and home calls to make in town, but covered much of the surrounding territory. My hours were so long that I rarely had supper before eight in the evening. Often, too exhausted to eat, I fell into bed hoping only to get a good night's sleep. The odds were against even that, for post-midnight emergency calls were more the rule than the exception.

In November I developed a severe form of angioneurotic edema. I puffed up like a balloon, with my skin breaking out into urticaria, itchy little red marks that made me look and feel as if I had chicken pox. I diagnosed my own condition, then consulted another doctor, who told me it was caused by extreme tension.

"What can I do?" I asked.

"Take it easier."

"I can't take it easier."

"You'll have to if you want to get rid of this," he said.

I never got completely rid of it. To this day my skin breaks out from time to time.

One night, soon after my ill-received church sermon, I said, "Mollie, let's do what we really want for once in our lives."

"You mean get out of here?"

"That's exactly what I mean."

"Where do you want to go?"

"As far away from Georgia and the deep South as I can."

"Like where?"

"Like Coronado, California," I said. "I'm going to telephone Jim Mushovic and see if there's an opening out there."

CHAPTER

4

I can't imagine two communities farther apart than Chickamauga, Georgia, and Coronado, California. The distance between them is more than physical. They are also widely separated in weather, appearance, economy, culture, geographical location, comfort, and sophistication. Chickamauga is Lower Slobbovia, Coronado Upper Utopia. Chickamauga's weather ranges from unbearable heat to miserable chill, Coronado's is consistently temperate. Chickamauga has the scrubby ugliness of the deep South's rural interior, Coronado the bright beauty of the southern California coast. Chickamauga is poor, Coronado rich. Chickamauga lives by its racial prejudice, Coronado is hardly aware of it. Chickamauga still remembers the Civil War, Coronado never knew it. Chickamauga has meager recreational facilities, Coronado a wide choice, ranging from beach to golf course, from theater to spectator sports. Chickamauga is isolated, Coronado five minutes by ferry from a big city and twenty minutes by car from another country. Chickamauga is narrow, Coronado sophisticated. Chickamauga's children want to get out, Coronado's to stay. Chickamauga has all the disadvantages of a small town and few of the advantages, Coronado all the advantages and few of the disadvantages. Chickamauga has little to offer, Coronado everything.

When we made this truly radical change in December, 1957, we ended all pretense of compromise with conscience. Chickamauga was our last effort to find something approximating the missionary life, and we could no more accept one than we could the other. The experiment had lasted six dismal months, during which I failed to have the satisfaction even of feeling I was doing something for someone.

We broke out of the cultural wilderness of Chickamauga into the cosmopolitan sparkle of Coronado with such enthusiasm that we were quickly and willingly caught up in the social life of the town's younger set. Thanks to Jim Mushovic, we could afford to do whatever we wanted. He brought me together with Dr. Mark Rhea, a young physician who had decided to sell his busy practice and do pathology. I purchased it and did well from the start. Patients were plentiful, payments prompt, and the hours reasonable. Except for emergencies, I could count on taking Thursday afternoons and Sundays off, and was rarely bothered at night.

Coronado likes young doctors with beautiful wives and small children. I was thirty and had three little boys. My wife was not only a beautiful brunette, but an outstanding tennis player as well. In Coronado this was important, for one of the city's most exclusive organizations is the Beach and Tennis Club at the spacious Del Coronado Hotel. Mollie, no longer forced to teach, played there often enough to regain much of her old form, and soon was enjoying the tennis groups in the area. The whole family spent many happy hours lounging in the lap of all the luxury the fine old hotel offered.

We joined the Crown Club, at the invitation of its plush membership of young dentists, doctors, lawyers, accountants, bankers, and other professional men. We bought a house on Country Club Lane with five bedrooms, three

36

baths, a patio, and a kitchen full of labor-saving devices. We had domestic help. We each had our own car, Mollie a station wagon, I a British-made convertible. We went to San Diego for theater and concerts and sports, and to Tijuana for bullfights and racing and *jai alai*. We weren't golfers, but our membership in the club enabled us to take part in its many social functions. One of my patients, who ran the Del Coronado Hotel boathouse, got me interested in sailing, and I spent my Thursday afternoons off on the water in a rented boat.

Although we had done an about-face from our earlier convictions, we did not neglect our faith. We joined the Methodist Church and were very active in the Sunday school. I became an executive in the local Boy Scouts and vice-president of the Parent-Teachers Association. In 1960, after being elected to the Coronado City Council, I became deeply involved in local politics. If I thought at all about my phantom missionary career, it was only in passing and without regrets.

In 1959 Jan, our daughter, was born. After her arrival, we thought seriously of getting a bigger house, although we had plenty of room. We finally bought an expensive lot on the beach, intending to build on it later. My gross income was well over $50,000 a year. I maintained a spacious office, and had a nurse and a secretary-receptionist. The secretary, Shirley Fleener, and her husband, Paul, a Navy flier, were among our close personal friends.

One cool, foggy night in 1959 the telephone rang while Mollie and I were sitting on the couch of our master bedroom in front of a roaring fire. "My wife's terribly sick, Dr. Turpin," a man said. "Can you come over?"

"Be right there," I said.

He was waiting for me when I pulled the car up at his house. As we walked in, he said, "My wife fainted and I can't pull her out of it."

She was lying motionless on the bed. Her breathing was

37

regular, her blood pressure and pulse normal. I examined her heart, lungs, abdomen, and eyes, then found she failed to respond to pinprick. There were no unusual odors.

"Has she had previous episodes like this?" I asked.

"Once. About three months ago. But not as bad."

"Has she been upset about anything?"

"Very nervous lately. Our baby's been sick. I'm gone a good deal of the time."

"There's nothing seriously wrong," I said. "Your wife has acute anxiety reactions. This is the body's way of temporarily escaping the pressures of our sophisticated society. She'll need to understand this more clearly. So will you. And you should plan to spend more time with her."

It was the same condition I had first seen in Santa Rosa. Since coming to Coronado I had had several cases, although not so many as I expected. But as I drove home in the fog that night, I wondered about it. Why did people suffer from this only on the West coast? I had never seen it anywhere else.

When I walked into my own house Mollie was in bed.

"What was it?" she asked.

"Acute anxiety. A young mother with too many pressures. Not knowing how to handle them, she crawled into a shell and pulled the lid over herself." I looked at Mollie, propped up on one elbow and staring at me. "Ever feel like doing that?"

"Sometimes," she said. "Things pile up—cub scouts, church activities, clubs, tennis, the house, the children, entertaining—"

"Are you happy?"

"Very."

"Is this what you want?"

"Oh, yes," she said. "And how about you?"

"Yes, sweetie," I said, "I'm quite happy."

But even as I spoke I wasn't so sure. We had had two years of plush, easy living, something we badly needed after

38

the lean years of medical school, internship, residency, and Chickamauga. We had arrived in Coronado emotionally and physically exhausted. Our batteries needed charging and our finances beefing up. We had accomplished both within months. Now, we had everything we had come to Coronado to get, plus the bonus of an eagerly-hoped-for baby daughter. Coronado had been good to us.

But had it been good *for* us? It had changed our standards, but had it made us lose them? As I lay in bed thinking that night, I wondered. I had no further illusions about becoming a missionary. I knew neither Mollie nor I had ever really wanted that. With all the talking we had done, we had succeeded only in kidding ourselves and each other. The missionary life was not for us. In that respect, we were more honest in Coronado than we had ever been, for we no longer rationalized about not being missionaries. Our church activity was what we wanted it to be, not what we thought it should be. We enjoyed it and considered it an integral part of our lives. It was as much pleasure as duty to tithe in our own way. We gave 5 per cent of our income to the church and 5 per cent to charity. We were doing all that might be expected of a successful young couple, perhaps more than most. We had, in fact, a perfect life in a perfect community. Yet something was lacking. I couldn't put my finger on it, but before I went to sleep that night I had the vague feeling that Coronado was only a step toward a goal, not the goal itself.

This was the beginning of a slow process of disenchantment which manifested itself in familiar ways. I jumped around so much Mollie dredged up her old nickname for me, "ye olde restless one." I couldn't sit still, couldn't concentrate, couldn't spend a quiet evening at home. I had to be on the go every minute, giving more and more time to outside activities and less and less to the family. I had painful attacks of the edema I had suffered in Chickamauga, with the urticaria sometimes covering my whole body. I slept so poorly that I welcomed odd-hour calls which gave me an excuse to get up and do something.

Mollie begged me to slow down. "Just when we have everything anyone could ever want," she said one night, "you're busy trying to kill yourself with work."

"I can't help it," I said. "I have to keep moving."

"Why?"

"I don't know."

"Aren't you happy?"

"If I'm not," I said, "it's nobody's fault but my own."

We had endless discussions of that kind, short, pointless, unsatisfactory. They worried us both, because they showed definite disagreement between us. All our past problems had been caused by outside conditions which we found equally frustrating. This time only I was dissatisfied. Mollie, busy being a wife, mother, hostess, athlete, clubwoman, and active church member, was perfectly happy. I certainly should have been. My medical practice was successful, my social, civic, and church activities full, my finances sound, my family content.

Every Sunday I conducted an adult class at the church. Each week I announced the subject for the following Sunday so that those who cared to could read up on it for discussion purposes. One morning I said, "The next lesson will be our annual study of missions," and that closed the day's class. As I was preparing to leave, Mrs. Lucille Bandel, a member of the class, came up and said, "Jim, why do we just talk about mission work?"

"What do you mean?" I said.

"Just what I say. I think it's a shame that we don't *do* something."

"Like what, in this beautiful place?"

"Like Tijuana," she said. "There are people we can almost see from here who really need our help. I know a woman who runs a school out in the canyon slums. We could do a lot for her."

"All I know about Tijuana is what the tourists know—the bullfights, the *jai alai*, the racing, the shopping on Revolucion Boulevard."

"That's all practically any of us knows. But I can take you to another Tijuana, to the Tijuana of Señora Maria Mesa of Casa de Todos. A wonderfully dedicated, inspiring woman. You should meet her."

"I'd like to," I said. "Let's start the class half an hour early next week and go down there when we finish."

The following week eight of us, including Lucille and her husband Kenny, and two other couples, got into the station wagon with Mollie and me to drive to Tijuana. Lucille was the only one who had traveled beyond the tourist area known to millions of Americans who have been in and out of this Mexican border town which seems small but is more than a third the size of San Diego in population. I had always taken its slums for granted, but never investigated them. To me Tijuana was a playground, not a social problem.

We drove south on the superhighway that connects San Diego with the Mexican border, past the big naval air base, then down along the coast for a few miles before turning southeast into the dry heat of the interior. We crossed the border and, once in Tijuana, followed Revolucion Boulevard. We passed tourist shops and night clubs until we reached Avenida Segunda, turning into the hills before reaching the *jai-alai* palace, the bull ring or Caliente race track. Soon we were on a winding street leading up into the bare dusty hills of Tijuana.

The road narrowed as we climbed, but there were no signs of poverty. We passed through a section of neat houses built close together, and small, well-kept lawns. Except for chattering children playing in the streets, few people were out in this residential area in the heat of midday. Those whom we saw stood quietly talking or slowly meandering along in their best Sunday clothes. Some of the

41

houses had automobiles in front, mostly five or more years old, for only the very rich in Mexico can afford brand-new American cars.

As we spiraled up we came to a cemetery, lush and green, with banks of flowers on stones and statues, and a caretaker watering one corner. When I commented on the beauty of the place, Lucille said, "That's for the rich people. We'll come to another one in a few minutes."

Halfway up the steep hill she told me to take a sharp right turn, off the main street onto a pock-marked road which was half-dust, half-decaying tar. It had once been paved, but obviously not for many years. Barefoot children, the boys in ragged shorts, the girls in faded dresses, played in front of chipped, cracked, windowless adobe houses built on tiny parched lots and standing in tight rows on both sides of the street. Here and there was a shop with a dust-caked window or two and a sign so dim it was unreadable even to anyone who knew Spanish.

"So these are the slums of Tijuana," I commented.

"The lower middle class lives here," Lucille said. "The slums are still ahead of us."

We leveled off for a hundred feet, then came to a rise, where we were greeted by a startling sight. Below and around us were hundreds of tiny huts and shacks and lean-tos which seemed to be tumbling all over each other on the steep, coarse hillsides and the canyon floors below. I stopped the car and stared at this city of wood and tin and plywood and cardboard and cloth and paper. Anything that would cover anything else was used as building material. As far as I could see, there was not one house in the strict sense of the word. Everything was made out of what had once been something else. There were no windows or doors, only openings, and most of the hovels were so close together that they held each other up.

"People actually live in those?" I murmured.

42

"Thousands and thousands," Lucille said. "Two and three families in each."

I pointed to a nearby plot of rock and bare earth covered with colored wooden crosses—blue, green, orange, red, lavender, yellow—and said, "That looks like a cemetery, too."

"It is," she said. "The poor people's cemetery."

"Why all the colors?"

"They can't afford flowers or stones or monuments or irrigation or caretakers, so they paint the crosses. It's the only memorial they have for their loved ones."

At the crest of the hill we turned to the right again, and started down along a rough, dusty road paralleling the ridge of the canyon's south wall. Far ahead lay the super highway and the lush green valley of southern California. The day was so clear we could even see the outlines of downtown San Diego's tall buildings. Directly ahead of us were a few houses similar to those we had passed on the pock-marked tar road. A wooden structure in the center stood out because it was the largest building in the area and bore a recent coat of white paint. As we came abreast of it, Lucille said, "Here we are."

Mollie leaned out and read aloud the sign: "Casa de Todos."

"That's right," Lucille said. "And here's Mrs. Mesa."

As we climbed out, a short, round woman, her gray hair pulled tightly back on her head, her faded silk dress bulging over her ample hips, her flat shoes tight about her swollen ankles, came out, followed by a group of perhaps twenty children, who stood quietly behind her as she greeted us. After Lucille introduced her, she told us in broken but quite understandable English the story of Casa de Todos.

"I am a trained social worker," she said. "My husband works for a trucking firm. We live in the center of town. One night thirteen years ago a boy of eight came to my door and asked if I would go with him to see his sick sister.

43

Thinking he lived nearby, I followed him all the way here —five miles and up the steepest hill in Tijuana."

She paused, then added, "I had never been in the canyons before. Now I spend more time here than at home."

She looked straight at me. "You are a doctor?" she asked. "Yes."

"We have a little clinic here in the afternoons. When the children go home from school, we give medicine to the sick. For a long time we had no one, but now a young Mexican doctor helps me some." She sighed. "He has no money, so we must pay him," she said. Then, still looking at me, she asked, "Would you like to see Casa de Todos?"

"Very much," I said.

We all followed her into the building. It was a cottage that had been trucked in from La Jolla, California, apparently by her husband. There was a classroom, where Mrs. Mesa taught during the week and conducted a simple service on Sundays, and behind that a much smaller room, used as a clinic. In the rear was a tiny kitchen and two half-empty storerooms.

"What do you need?" I asked.

She shook her head. "So much—so much," she said. "These people are unbelievably poor. They need food, clothes, medicine, care. Dr. Rivera does what he can to help, but his time is limited. I suppose yours is too, Dr. Turpin."

"I'd like to help," I said. "I'll come next Thursday afternoon, if you like." For once, I thought, I can give up sailing.

Mrs. Mesa looked up into my eyes, her gaze hypnotically steady, and said, "You will not regret it."

We followed her down into the canyon for a closer look at the huts and the people living in them. There were more of each than I had expected. It was so crowded we had to pick our way along, walking lopsided because everything was angled by the sharp incline of the hill. The men sat around in the sun, talking in dull monotones and staring at

44

nothing with the empty eyes of the perpetually unem-
ployed. Mrs. Mesa told us that most were from the rural
sections of Baja California, the Mexican state of which Tijuana is the metropolis. After crop failures, they had come
to Tijuana in search of work, but all they found were misery, starvation, and sickness. Their wives greeted Mrs. Mesa
warmly and smiled wanly at us when she explained who
we were. Worried, tired from too much to do and too little
rest, many bearing the marks of serious illness, they were all
old before their time. I felt terribly sorry for them, but the
hardest thing for me to take was the sight of the children.
The whole canyon seemed alive with them, some healthy
enough, but too many potbellied from undernourishment
or suffering from the hacking cough of respiratory diseases.

No one had much to say on the way home, but I sensed
that Lucille Bandel had done me a great favor. For the first
time since the beginning of my restlessness in the plush life
of Coronado I saw a way to justify my existence by giving
a little of myself to something which truly needed me. I
would see a good deal of Casa de Todos and Casa de Todos
a good deal of me.

CHAPTER

5

The following Thursday, as soon as I could get away from
morning rounds and office hours, Mollie and I drove to
Tijuana in the station wagon, which we had loaded with
whatever we could collect. She had gone around town
gathering used toys, and I had a big carton of sample drugs.
We also talked the Hotel Del Coronado kitchen and Anderson's bakery into giving us a trunkful of day-old bread and

pan dulce—sweet Mexican rolls—and they promised more for the weeks to follow.

At Casa de Todos Mrs. Mesa introduced us to Dr. Alfonso Rivera Diaz and a young Mexican nurse who helped in the clinic. I stayed outside a few minutes just to see the reaction of the children to the things we had brought. A hug on one leg by a black-eyed boy of five—my reward for a *pan dulce*—brought a lump to my throat and drove me into the clinic. One more such gesture of affection would have broken me down in tears.

As the weeks and months went by, I spent more and more time at Casa de Todos. At first I went only on Thursdays, sometimes with Mollie, sometimes with others, most often alone. Then I began leaving the office early on Saturdays until I split the day equally between Coronado and Tijuana, and finally was going to Tijuana without stopping at the office at all except for emergencies. After a while I started heading for Tijuana right from church on Sundays, giving me a full day and two half days a week there. Often I stayed well into the evening, sometimes not returning home until after midnight. I knew this was unfair to Mollie and the children, but I couldn't help myself. Casa de Todos drew and held me involuntarily. Once there, I completely lost track of time.

One spring day in 1961 we had an unusually busy Thursday afternoon, in which we found two patients with undiagnosed diabetes, a small boy with a hydrocele on which we later operated, and several people with odd fungus diseases of the skin. As we were preparing to go home, a young woman came in with two children, each gasping for breath. Realizing we had to work fast, Dr. Rivera took one and I the other. The skins of both small patients gave off intense heat, their nostrils flared with their labored breathing, and it was obvious they were suffering from severe bilateral pneumonia.

While the nurse and I quickly constructed a crude steam

tent of blankets and plastic tubes, Dr. Rivera administered massive doses of penicillin. I added a mist to the steam to help relax the breathing passages, and we put the children inside. While the nurse sponged their fiery bodies from time to time, we waited four hours, tensely wondering if we had been too late. Finally, first one child then the other began to show the hopeful signs we prayed for—pink lips, slower, deeper, less labored breathing, and a break in temperature. We all sighed with relief, for now Dr. Rivera could tell the mother her babies would be all right.

It was half an hour before midnight when I climbed into my car to drive home. On the way, I had the most exhilarating feeling of absolute satisfaction I had ever known. There wasn't a shadow of a doubt that these children would have died if I hadn't been there. As I sped north on the wide superhighway I wondered how many other children in how many other parts of the world were dying because there was no doctor to help them through such a crisis. I thought about the people who came to see me in Coronado —the anxious, the neurotic, the hypochondriacs, the men and women who found it hard to live with the stresses of prosperity. They didn't need me. San Diego County was full of doctors as efficient as I and better qualified emotionally to cope with their problems, real and imagined.

I wasn't qualified emotionally, not any more. Coronado, lovely as it was, offered an embarrassment of riches, an abundance of material pleasures and opportunities unavailable in comparable breadth anywhere else I knew, but Coronado could get along without me. Only a Casa de Todos could satisfy me now, although even that was not enough. Other doctors would be glad to help Mrs. Mesa; I had to be where the need was greater. I didn't know exactly what I would do as I reached Orange Avenue in Coronado and headed for home that night, but it would be something radically different, something that would give me pleasure in the sheer joy of being needed. I decided to say nothing to Mollie until I had thought things through. She had trouble enough trying to understand my discontent.

There was no religious motivation in my desire to leave Coronado, no recurrence of my old ambition to become a missionary. My faith in my church was genuine, but I no longer intended to try to transmit that faith to others, or to convert the heathen while healing his ills. I wanted to go overseas, preferably somewhere in Asia, not because it was still a fertile field for missionary work but because the need for medical service was so great. In that spring of 1961 I thought often of Papa Duke, not only needed but loved by the people of Knott County in Kentucky. He worked hard for little material return, but nothing could pay for the wealth of satisfaction he derived from doing so much for so many. That was what I had missed in Chickamauga and in Coronado, what I had enjoyed in Tijuana.

Although Papa Duke had always been my idol, I could not live as he had lived. Chickamauga proved that. If I had the temperament to be a country doctor I could have succeeded even there by being simply a doctor instead of trying to be a reformer, too. Papa Duke would have accepted Chickamauga for what it was, not try to change in six months the habits of a century. No, Papa Duke's life was not for me. I needed something else.

Saving the two children that night at Casa de Todos was the first of two incidents which had a profound influence on my life. The second came a few days later in my office. I had returned from lunch a little early and was sitting with my feet on the desk thumbing through a medical magazine. Suddenly I ran across a familiar verse that hit me right between the eyes. I don't know how many times I had read it before, but now these words of John Donne's took on new meaning:

"*No man is an island, entire in itself;*
    Every man is a piece out of the continent, a part
        of the main;

> If a clod be washed away by the sea, Europe is
>   the less;
> As well as if a promontory were;
> As well as if a manor of thy friend's or of thine
>   own were;
> Any man's death diminishes me, for I am involved
>   in mankind;
> And therefore never send to know for whom the
>   bell tolls, it tolls for thee."

Two of these lines especially might have been written just for me as I wrestled with the torment in my heart—"No man is an island" and "Any man's death diminishes me, for I am involved in mankind." I repeated them over and over, and was still staring at them when Martha Oldendorph, my office nurse, interrupted my reverie with, "Your patients are here, Doctor."

One of the patients that day was Lieutenant (j.g.) Robin Bacon, just back from a six-months cruise to the Orient aboard an aircraft carrier. He and his wife, whose baby I had delivered, were members of our church. Once a year he came in for a routine checkup. As usual when he returned from a cruise, we talked about the places he had been and the people he had seen.

"I spent four days in Hong Kong," he said. "Did you know that was chosen the refugee capital of the world last year?"

"I read it somewhere," I said.

"Have you any idea what that means?"

"In terms of what?"

"In terms of the way people live," Robin said. "They sleep in the streets, on rooftops, in cardboard boxes. Jim, there are families sharing the same cardboard box in eight-hour shifts, three families to a box. They eat out of garbage cans, they sell their daughters to keep alive, they suffer from horrible diseases which they pass around like Typhoid

49

Mary. You can't imagine what it's like until you have seen for yourself."

He talked about Hong Kong all through the examination, and when he left I thought about Hong Kong. I was still thinking about it when I reached home. That night I read about it in a San Diego *Evening Tribune* feature story, which told of thousands of refugees stopped at the Hong Kong border and sent back to China. The paper ran a picture of weeping mothers carrying small, skinny children back across the river.

Mollie was finishing the dinner dishes, Jan was in her high chair, and the boys were playing outside. "Sweetie," I said, "let's go to Hong Kong."

For a full minute Mollie looked at me, then said, "You're serious, aren't you?"

"Yes, I am."

I handed her the newspaper. After she read the story and studied the picture, I told her about Robin Bacon's visit that afternoon. Later, when the children were in bed, we talked well into the night, and the more I talked the more convinced I became that Hong Kong would give me what I had been seeking all my life. I didn't have to tell Mollie of my growing discontent—she was well aware of that—but we talked at length about it, and about the meaning of John Donne's verse.

"Why must we go all the way to Hong Kong?" Mollie said. "Can't you get the same satisfaction from Casa de Todos?"

"It's too close."

"You're needed there."

"But not irreplaceable. I can get others to go there as often as I do."

"Perhaps you can find a rural practice in California."

"It wouldn't work," I said.

Although her first impulse was to resist, Mollie, as anxious for me to find contentment and satisfaction as I was myself, gradually shifted from arguments against Hong Kong to questions about where to start, how to raise money, where to get help, how the children would react, and other such practical details. It took her several days to reach that point, but once she realized the depth of my own desire and determination, she transformed herself from devil's advocate to willing assistant.

We considered the organizations with which we might work, for at that time it never occurred to us to go to Hong Kong on our own. We sought a charitable group which had no government or denominational affiliation. The three which interested us most were the World Health Organization, MEDICO, and Project Hope. We wrote WHO first, and soon received an answer that it was interested only in public-health and sanitation experts. This was not for me, since I was a general practitioner.

Then we tried Dr. Tom Dooley's fine organization, MEDICO. Having read his books, I greatly admired this young jungle doctor who had died of cancer in 1960. Had he lived, I would have gone anywhere necessary to meet him. We waited more than a month, but had no reply from MEDICO, and, in fact, never did hear. This left Project Hope, which answered promptly, but had no openings at the time. They put me on a so-called "stand-by" basis, but this meant an indefinite wait.

In the meantime, we went about the business of clearing up our affairs in Coronado. I resigned from the City Council and took steps to sell our house, our cars, the lot we had bought on the beach, and my practice. Although I suppose they thought we were crazy at first, our friends were thoughtful and understanding when they realized why we were leaving.

But three months after we decided to go, we still hadn't made much progress. We heard about an organization called World Vision, which, although very evangelistic, had a policy of letting its people go where they wanted to go and develop their work in their own way. We were also told that World Vision provided financing. Mollie and I went to their headquarters in Los Angeles, where we met their medical directors, Dr. Bill Van Valen and Dr. Ken Kroll. Both were impressive, dynamic young men whom we enjoyed immensely, and we spent the better part of the day with them. They agreed that Hong Kong needed what we had to offer, and were willing to finance us to some extent. However, we were expected to raise as much as we could ourselves and go to them for the rest only when we had exhausted our own resources. We might have been willing to join them on that basis except for the contract we were asked to sign. Among other things, it contained a clause reading something like, "I accept the Bible word for word. I believe it exactly as written. I don't question anything it says." There was also something about baptism contrary to any of the teachings we had had. Neither Mollie nor I could accept these conditions.

We parted from Bill Van Valen and Ken Kroll the best of friends—we still keep in touch with them—but we didn't join their organization. On the way home Mollie and I discussed our next move. We toyed with the possibility of going into missionary work, for if we could consider anything like World Vision, we could certainly think in terms of our own church. But we were only talking. We had long since discarded the missionary field, and we knew it would be unethical and dishonest for us to reconsider, since our only motive would be to get financing. Still, Mollie said, there must be another way. Later, she suggested one.

After dinner one night she said, "Why don't we start our own organization?"

"How can we do that?" I asked.

"Well, up in Los Angeles we were willing to consider raising as much as we could, with World Vision paying the rest. We know people around the country, and we have some money of our own. Let's raise it all ourselves."

Now her eyes were shining, and the words poured out. We had friends everywhere—the South, the Midwest, up and down the Pacific coast. I had patients from many parts of the country, for Coronado, full of active and retired Navy personnel, had few actual natives. Almost everyone came from somewhere else. As Mollie talked, my own hopes lifted. There were all sorts of ways in which we could start an organization of our own.

A day or two later Jon Gudmonds, a drug salesman representing the Strassenberg Laboratories, stopped in at the office to brief me on their newer products.

"I won't be around here much longer," I said. "My wife and I are planning to take the family to Hong Kong and work among the refugees."

"Tremendous idea," he said. "You do something like that and I'll get you the medicine you need."

"You will?"

"There isn't a laboratory in the country that wouldn't be glad to help. They'll send samples until they're coming out of your ears. By the way, what are you calling your group?"

"We haven't got a name yet."

"Get one soon," he said. "You can't raise money without a name."

That night Jon came over to help us figure out a name. "Hope," "Care," "World Vision," "Medico" all seemed so natural, especially since they were already taken. Mollie suggested "compassion," but that was too long. "Love" sounded pretentious. There were so many different kinds of love that the word had become distorted and twisted and misshapen. I was thumbing through the dictionary when I came across "concern," and that hit us all. It was neither too long nor too short, it had never been misused, and it told the story. Then Mollie suggested borrowing "project" from Project Hope, and we had our name.

"Project Concern." It sounded right.

CHAPTER

6

Jack Wills, a pessimistic young lawyer, had spent many futile hours trying to talk me out of what seemed to him an absolutely insane idea. We had dinner with him and his wife, Beverly, who was Mollie's best friend in Coronado, a few nights after Project Concern was born. When we told him we had a name and were planning to raise money, he said, "You're really going through with this, aren't you?"

"Of course," I said.

"Well, then," he said, "you've got to have legal direction. You can't just go out and raise money, you know. You have to incorporate, set up a board of directors, elect officers, arrange for income-tax exemption, be recognized as a charitable medical organization, and heaven knows what else. Now here's what we'll do—"

So Jack Wills set the legal wheels in motion. It would be several months before all the proper papers were drawn and signed and witnessed and sealed, but with the preliminaries taken care of we could go ahead with our plans. In early May, 1961, we released a story to the Coronado *Journal* that I was resigning from the City Council in order to form Project Concern and set up refugee clinics in Hong Kong. The story wasn't picked up by the wire services, but it might as well have been. Everyone in town read the *Journal*, and my patients began passing the word about Project Concern to their families and friends elsewhere in the country.

One, Mrs. Ross Wilhite whose baby I had recently delivered, sent a clipping of the story to her parents in Winnetka, Illinois, Mr. and Mrs. Harry D. Thorsen. I soon had a letter from Dorothy Thorsen, telling me how deeply interested she and her friends on Chicago's North Shore were in what we proposed to do. She offered to get a group together to help support Project Concern. We had similar word from Jacksonville, where we knew people who had once lived in Coronado.

One day Paul Fleener telephoned from Manhattan, Kansas. Out of the Navy, he was now news director of KSAC, the Kansas State University radio station.

"What's this all about?" he asked.

After I told him, he said, "Shirley and I want to work with you. We can be out there in a month."

"Wonderful," I said. "Only make sure this is what you really want."

"I've been in Hong Kong, Jim. I think you've got a great idea, and we want to be part of it."

He promised in the meantime to start a Project Concern chapter in Manhattan. Later, he wrote that a doctor and other friends in his home town of Greensburg, Kansas, were spearheading a similar chapter there. Soon checks began coming in from both places.

In a letter from Ashland, Kentucky, my dad wrote that he and Mother were proud and happy, and were busy organizing a Project Concern group there. The next time I talked to them on the telephone, Mother said, "We felt you wanted to do something like this all your life, but we didn't want to say anything. Now we're so glad you've made this decision."

Helen Williamson, Mollie's mother, seemed just as pleased. She and many of our friends had already built an Atlanta chapter. Helen had come out to Coronado to be my medical secretary. At the time of her death in 1964 she was running our Project Concern office there.

The Active 20–30 Club of Coronado, made up of businessmen in their twenties and thirties, were the first local organization to back us. I had once been a member of this group, and so had Paul. They helped raise money and publicize Project Concern, not only by word of mouth but in any other way they could.

Shirley and Paul Fleener arrived in Coronado late in July, just in time to join Jack Wills, Mollie, and me on our first board of directors. We were now operating out of an office on Orange Avenue which had been donated by Jim Darnell. We were using plain stationery, with the name Project Concern and our post-office box number as a return address. I thought we should have an emblem, and drew up one with two circles, a cross, and a caduceus, but it wasn't very good. John Sarber, the chairman of the San Diego-Coronado Project Concern chapter, knew a tremendously creative industrial designer named Joe Manno, who was eager to help us. He drew a caduceus on top of the world with just one circle, and we quickly adopted it, eliminating the cross because we wanted to be universal, not tied to any one religious faith.

I promised Mrs. Mesa not to go to Hong Kong without getting another American doctor to help her at Casa de Todos. I found one by accident during a fund-raising meeting we ran at the Del Coronado Hotel featuring Dr. Bill Van Valen, our friend from World Vision. He came down to show slides of the jungle hospital in Laos, where he had worked with Dr. Tom Dooley. Bill spoke for about three-quarters of an hour, during which he pointed out that we hoped to open hospitals and clinics much like Dr. Dooley's. I followed with a brief talk, mentioning, among other things, that one of my biggest regrets was leaving Casa de Todos.

When the meeting ended, Dr. Pat Dunklee, who had four children of her own, came to me and asked, "Who's going to replace you at Tijuana?"

"We don't have anyone yet," I said.

"I've been sick," she said, "and now I need something to occupy my time. Will I do?"

"You certainly will."

56

The next Thursday I took her to Tijuana. She and Mrs. Mesa liked each other on sight, and soon she was going down there nearly every day. As I became more occupied with Project Concern I had less and less time for Casa de Todos, but my mind was at ease about leaving because I knew it was in such good hands.

I made my first direct Hong Kong contact through Mother, perhaps the last person in the world I would expect to know anyone there. She told me a high-school classmate of mine had married Peter Jenkins, an Englishman who is medical director of the Junk Bay Medical Relief Society. He runs the Haven of Hope Tuberculosis Sanitarium in the New Territories of Hong Kong, with the help of an amazing Norwegian nurse named Annie Skau, who stands six feet and weighs two hundred and fifty pounds. I corresponded with Peter and his wife, Billie, and both encouraged me to go. Through them I contacted Dr. Gordon Addington, an American who also liked our idea.

Before taking the family, I wanted to make a survey trip to Hong Kong. I also hoped to visit Dr. Gordon Seagrave, the famous "Burma surgeon" at NamKham, his hospital in northeastern Burma, but since bandits were operating in that area and I couldn't get assurance of safe travel, I decided against going there. Actually, I still didn't even know how I would get to Hong Kong. We had collected about three thousand dollars and were receiving some six hundred a month at this point, but I hadn't touched any of it, and didn't want to for that purpose. I had to figure out some other way of financing this preliminary trip.

There was a cholera outbreak in Hong Kong that summer, and I had already written a New York pharmaceutical firm for vaccine. The company agreed to send it to San Diego if I could get it the rest of the way. I telephoned Admiral Red Yeager of the Amphibious Base on the Silver Strand in Coronado, and he promised to do what he could. The shipment reached San Diego, and was still there while

I was trying to dope out a way to go to Hong Kong myself. Somebody suggested the Navy might fly me out on the same plane with the vaccine, and fly me back later. I telephoned the Admiral again, and when he got permission from the State and Navy departments, I had my transportation. The only trouble was that nobody, including the Admiral himself, had any idea when a plane would be going to Hong Kong or how good my chances were of staying on it. I could be bumped off anywhere along the way, and, once in Hong Kong, might have to stay much longer than I intended.

I guess everybody in Coronado was aware of the problem, since nothing remained a secret there for very long. Furthermore, it being a big Navy center, the whole town understood what Navy transportation meant in terms of possible delay. For lack of anything else, I sat tight and waited, but we all wished there were some way I could go to Hong Kong and back without wasting so much time.

One afternoon Mollie and I were having lunch on the patio overlooking the tennis courts at the Del Coronado Hotel when John Alessio, the owner, stopped at our table. A former Tijuana newsboy who had made a fortune in San Diego, he had recently bought and injected new life into the hotel. He and I had become very friendly after I began going to Casa de Todos. This was one of many Tijuana projects which he helped support.

"Hello, Jim—Mrs. Turpin," he said. "It's good to see you."

We chatted a few minutes, then he said, "I hear you want to go to Hong Kong."

"I'm standing by for Navy transportation," I said.

He handed me a business card. "Call this number," he said. "It's my travel agent. He has a round-trip airplane ticket for you." Then he stood up, waved off our thanks, said good-bye, and left.

That very afternoon Mollie called me at the Coronado

Hospital, where I was delivering a baby, to tell me the Navy had space for me. I telephoned the Admiral, thanked him profusely, and said that I had decided to fly by commercial airline.

Three days later, while descending over Hong Kong, I stared at this gorgeous city and thought, "How can a place so beautiful need the services Project Concern intends to give?" I soon found out that Hong Kong's beauty is skin deep, for beneath the breath-taking façade she exhibits to the casual visitor are some of the world's most horrible slums.

I was greeted at the airport by a reception committee of thirteen. Bonnie and Gordon Addington then had six children, Billie and Peter Jenkins three, and all were waiting for me when I arrived. Although I hadn't seen her since high school, I recognized Billie Jenkins immediately. The others were strangers to me.

Peter Jenkins and Gordon Addington are both doctors and about the same height—perhaps a couple of inches short of six feet—but the resemblance ends there. Except for Peter's very British mustache, he would seem to be the American and Gordon the Englishman. Peter is a quick-moving, fast-talking, articulate man with sharp eyes that dart about and take in everything in range. At a hundred and seventy pounds, he is stocky and powerful-looking. Gordon, heavier and nowhere nearly so animated, is quiet, almost phlegmatic, with deliberate speech, a steady gaze, and a slow smile. They were glad to see me, eager to show me around, and ready to do what they could for me.

There was so much to see and do and learn in the two weeks I planned to stay that, much as I would like to have met the "Burma Surgeon," I was just as happy I had called off that part of the trip. One week in Hong Kong would not have been nearly enough. In two, I could find out where to start, what to plan, what to aim for.

The areas that impressed me most as possible sites for

clinics were the Walled City of Kowloon and the typhoon shelters. The Walled City, forbidden to strangers because so many who went in alone never came out, is a no-man's land created in 1898. For some strange reason it was not included in the agreement between Great Britain and China when the British assumed control of the New Territories. The Hong Kong police have no jurisdiction over it, and neither has anyone else. It must be one of the smelliest, filthiest, most disease-ridden hell holes on earth. Covering an area of about six city blocks square, this jungle of misery has an estimated 50,000 people living in such close quarters they hardly have room to turn around. The buildings seem on top of each other, the streets so narrow you can stand on one side and almost touch the other.

A Chinese pastor named Reverend David Yen and Mrs. Donnithorne, an English woman whom I met through Peter and Gordon, took me through the Walled City for the first time. We entered what appeared to be a doorway on a Kowloon street, which led to a little flight of concrete steps. In the dark maze of filth at the bottom the stench was indescribable. With no running water, no restrictions, no attempt to control sanitation, children relieve themselves wherever and whenever nature calls. In order to keep from stepping on the remains, you must pick your way carefully along sidewalks and cross streets the width of small alleys. Only rain or waste water occasionally poured from the eight-by-ten-foot hovels where people live washes away the sewage—or makes it worse. Since the buildings are so close together the sun rarely reaches the street. It is always dark in daytime, pitch black at night. The only transportation is by foot; everything must be taken in and out manually.

Mrs. Donnithorne had a small clinic near the outskirts. With the help of a Chinese doctor who came in once or twice a week and was available for emergencies, she handled most of the case load herself.

"We need a hundred clinics in the Walled City," she told

me. "Whatever else you plan for Hong Kong, I hope you'll try to do something here."

"This is one of the first places I would consider," I said.

The location of Mrs. Donnithorne's clinic was bizarre, to say the least. Directly upstairs was an opium den and right across the narrow road a house of prostitution. This wasn't unusual for the Walled City, but not knowing that at the time, I made a point of commenting on it when I later announced our intentions of running a clinic there. The story went out on the wire services and came back months later to haunt us.

While not so ghastly nor so frightening as the Walled City, the typhoon shelters were nearly as crowded, just as smelly, and fully as much in need of medical facilities. About 135,000 people live aboard junks jammed so close together that at some points you can walk miles over water and never get your feet wet. Thousands of folks are born, live out their lives, and die without touching dry land. More important to me was the utter absence of doctors. There were public clinics in the city, but the boat people never went near them.

The Yaumati shelter and the Aberdeen shelter are the two largest. The Aberdeen shelter is better known, for this is where the picturesque restaurants and many tourist attractions are located. The Yaumati shelter has the most—and the poorest—people. The largest shelter in Hong Kong, with a population of about 32,000, it is a fantastic slum teeming with the hungry, the diseased, and the poverty-stricken. After several trips around Yaumati, I decided that a floating clinic there would serve a badly-needed purpose. Peter and Gordon agreed.

They introduced me to British public-health and American consulate officials whose cooperation would be essential. One of the men most helpful was an American named Herman Washington, who headed the Refugee and Migration Unit of our consulate in Hong Kong. Washington was a warm, scholarly, stoop-shouldered Negro who stood well over six feet, weighed more than two hundred pounds, and talked and dressed like an ivy leaguer. He was pleased with our plans, and delighted to help in any way he could.

"There aren't many Americans willing to work among the poor of Hong Kong," he said. "Especially people with practical ideas they can carry out themselves."

"Do you think our ideas are practical?" I asked.

"Indeed I do. You have picked two of the areas most desperately in need of your services. And there are no better ambassadors of good will than doctors with your sincerity of purpose."

We talked at length about the requirements for practicing medicine in Hong Kong. I would need a British license, which Herman suggested I obtain in Canada.

"They give examinations regularly," he said. "As a practicing physician you should have no trouble. However, I would advise you to familiarize yourself with public-health problems. It is a separate profession in the United States, but the British consider it a branch of medical training and include it in their examinations."

I made a note to study up on the subject, but when I got home I learned that the six-day medical exams necessary for a Canadian license would begin within forty-eight hours, so I flew to Winnipeg and took my chances. Three months later, in January, 1962, I received word that I had flunked public health, but could repeat that section alone when the next exams were given in March. I spent weeks boning up, and that time I passed it.

In the meantime, there was much to do. The problem of transportation had been bothering us ever since we had had to arrange with the Admiral to fly the cholera vaccine to Hong Kong in a Navy plane. We were lucky that time, but not everything is compact enough to be flown out. Some items must be shipped, and shipping costs halfway around the globe are high.

Paul Fleener came up with the answer to that problem. During his Navy days he had served aboard the aircraft carrier *Shangri-La* with Commander Hop Hansen. Hansen started Operation Handclasp, a remarkable organization which, without publicity, fanfare, or even direct authorization from the Navy, quietly sends drugs, supplies, food, clothing, toys, and other items to needy areas throughout the world aboard Navy ships on a space-available basis.

Operation Handclasp, now Project Handclasp, began after the Korean War, when Hansen learned that American charitable organizations overseas were forced to spend much of their capital on transportation. Since United States Navy ships often have plenty of cargo room, Hansen, a career officer with connections all over the fleet, asked skippers he knew to carry what they could. Few Navy ships shove off from American ports today without first notifying Operation Handclasp where they are going and how much they can handle. In this manner, tons of supplies are shipped free all over the world. Officially, the Navy Department has nothing to do with Operation Handclasp, but unofficially the Navy is well aware of the good it does and the friends it makes for the United States.

When Hansen came to San Diego, Paul and I went over to see him, and he promised to put us on his list of Hong Kong groups as soon as we were settled there. He is now one of Project Concern's strongest supporters, and saves us thousands of dollars in transportation costs every year.

We were incorporated as a charitable organization in November, 1961, which meant that we could register with the Internal Revenue Department and our donors could claim income-tax deductions for funds they sent us. By this time about nine hundred dollars a month was coming in, and we had more new chapters. Doctors in two nearby communities, Dr. Elbert Hayes of Imperial Beach and Dr. William Boyce of Escondido, were especially helpful in those early days of our existence.

I decided to take a nationwide promotion trip, using my personal funds so as not to touch any of the money meant for our Hong Kong clinics. We expanded our board of directors from five to nine, and voted to employ Ed Flynn of Los Angeles as our promotion director. He arranged my itinerary, which included all the places that had Project Concern chapters, with particular emphasis on Chicago, Atlanta, Houston, and Jacksonville. I saw the Thorsens in Chicago and, through them, met Mr. and Mrs. W. Clement Stone, without whom Project Concern might never have got off the ground, and even now would find it difficult to keep going.

Mr. Stone and his wife Jessie have the Foundation which has given us more financial support than any other single source. Head of Combined Insurance, he has authored and co-authored several books on the subject of positive mental attitudes, of which he is a great advocate. The recognition of both the Stones in what we were trying to do got Project Concern off to a flying start. Without their help, we couldn't have left for Hong Kong as soon as we did.

In Houston I had a big lift from Jimmy Morris, a former All-American football player at Georgia Tech. In New York, where we hired professional public-relations help, I stayed at the Overseas Press Club, and spoke there and on various radio and television programs. I was amazed at the interest people showed in what was no more than an idea generated by an obscure doctor in a small southern California town. By June, 1962, before we had examined a patient, taken a temperature, or prescribed a pill, we were collecting $2,500 a month.

From San Francisco came an invitation to speak before a group of Chinese businessmen who had read about Project Concern in *China World*, the Chinese-language newspaper there. Mr. C. H. Quok, the publisher, had written an editorial about me, and Dr. Dennis Wong, who came from Hong Kong and was an honor graduate in pharmacy of the

University of California, had organized the group. While I was in San Francisco, Dennis suggested going to Hong Kong and working with us for six months. I couldn't have had a more perfect combination—a Chinese pharmacist who knew the city.

At about this time I had a call from Dr. Gerald Easton, a Coronado optometrist who had started a campaign to send used eyeglasses to Project Concern. He thought it would be good publicity if we got ourselves pictured with a Chinese student wearing glasses. We telephoned California Western University in San Diego, which had several Chinese-born undergraduates. A girl from Hong Kong named Sharon Wong (no relation to Dennis—Wong is a popular family name among the Chinese) had heard of us and was glad to cooperate. This later developed into one of our finest Hong Kong friendships with her parents, Dr. and Mrs. Daniel Wong.

We planned to go in August when, at the rate contributions were coming in, our bank account would top $20,000. Things were moving well, with the chapters sending money monthly, and our headquarters in the hands of Florence Liebhaber, an experienced office manager who joined us as a volunteer. Another volunteer, Florance Mitchell, was organizing a team of drug sorters. Sorting drugs is a tiresome, time-consuming job which became increasingly important as more and more samples arrived from pharmaceutical houses and laboratories all over the country. Drugs and medicines poured in from many sources, including Abbott, Smith, Kline and French, Ciba, Schering, Savage, Johnson and Johnson, and Lederle. Some of the material was priceless, some worthless, and finding a practical way of quickly deciding which was which was a major problem that took a year to solve.

We left for Hong Kong aboard the Pacific and Orient liner, *Arcadia*, on August 10, 1962. Mollie, the four children, Shirley and Paul Fleener and I went by ship, with

Dennis Wong following by plane. He was scheduled to arrive in Hong Kong the day after we landed. About one hundred of our sponsors attended a farewell party arranged by Chet Lighthizer, chairman of our Los Angeles chapter, just before we shoved off from Long Beach. We all made brief speeches, but everybody was too excited to talk much and no one had anything very earth-shaking to say. There was a slight last-minute delay when our Hong Kong visas were late arriving, but otherwise everything went smoothly. When we finally got settled aboard for the great adventure, Paul and I took account of stock and found the results satisfactory.

We had a headquarters office in Coronado, with a capable office manager in Florence Liebhaber, assisted by Mollie's mother, Helen Williamson, who had moved from Atlanta. We had a professional promotion director in Ed Flynn. We had about twenty-five hundred dollars a month coming in on a regularly scheduled basis. We had pharmaceutical houses all over the country sending drugs, and a promise from Operation Handclasp to ship them. We had the 20–30 Club in Coronado, the Chinatown committee in San Francisco, and active chapters in Los Angeles, Chicago, Atlanta, Jacksonville, Houston, Ashland, Kentucky, and Greensburg and Manhattan, Kansas. We had our health, our hopes, and our dreams, and we were all together, facing a new life and a new future in new surroundings on the other side of the world.

I couldn't wait to get there.

CHAPTER

7

Three days out of Hong Kong I got a cable from Peter Jenkins and Gordon Addington which read: "Don't talk to anyone on arrival before seeing us." When we landed Peter said, "Jim, the police are very unhappy about Project Concern."

"Why?"

"Because of what you said about having seen a clinic beneath an opium den and across from a house of prostitution."

"I thought it was unusual enough to mention," I said.

"Did you specify the Walled City?"

"I'm sure I did."

"The wire stories didn't," Peter said. "Since the police can't go into the Walled City they don't care what anyone says about it. But they're proud of the job they've done controlling narcotics and prostitution everywhere else. When your statement appeared in the Hong Kong papers, they reacted with wires suggesting that if Dr. Turpin would supply the addresses of such establishments they would be happy to curtail these illegal activities."

"Oh, my."

"And that isn't all," Peter went on. "You're in trouble with the medical authorities, too. A reporter on one of the papers asked Dr. D. J. M. MacKenzie, the head of the Hong Kong Medical and Health Department, if you were registered to practice here, and he said you weren't."

"That was my fault, Jim," Gordon said. "I forgot to tell you a Canadian license isn't good here. You have to send to London for a British license."

"After talking to Dr. MacKenzie," said Peter, "a couple of the newspapers made it look as if the medical people were

67

deliberately obstructing your plans. One criticized the British government for trying to stop a group of dedicated young people from the States, including a Chinese pharmacist, from helping the refugees here by refusing you a license. The papers are taking sides, with you as the issue. Reporters are waiting in the ship's lounge for you right now."

In the midst of this mess, mostly of my own making, I spent so many hours of the next few weeks apologizing, explaining, being interviewed, filling out applications, and seeking advice and solace from people like Peter and Gordon and Herman Washington that I hardly had time for anything else. It would have been pretty discouraging except for the progress we made.

Dr. and Mrs. Wong, the parents of the California Western University girl we had met in San Diego through Dr. Easton, gave us the use of a ten-room house at 25 Oxford Road in Kowloon, and we all moved in. This was our home, office, and headquarters for months, and the garage was our warehouse until we outgrew it.

Every day we learned something new. Mollie hired an amah named Ague, who came from a little squatter village on the other side of the road. This settlement, which dropped back into a canyon for about a mile and a half, reminded me of Tijuana. The people lived in lean-tos, made mostly of cardboard with burlap or tar roofs. At one point the street was lined with soft-drink advertisements, one family using a Coke carton for its wall, another a Pepsi sign, still another a Ne-Hi box. We never threw cardboard cartons away. Ague always knew somebody who needed them for walls.

Paul, chairman of our committee in charge of practically everything nonmedical, entered us in a Chinese-language school. Of the four of us—Mollie, Shirley, Paul, and me—I was by far the worst student. Never much of a linguist anyhow, I found Chinese particularly puzzling. The dialects all have subtle nuances, with word meanings often depending not on accent but on the inflection of sound. A word spoken with a rising sound means one thing, falling something else, level something else again. Some words have six or seven different meanings. This is why the Chinese always seem to the uninitiated Occidental to be arguing. The rise and fall of their voices give the impression that they're screaming at each other when they're simply talking normally. A good ear for music helps and Mollie, who has one, did quite well. But I'm tone deaf and never could get the hang of it.

One of our first telephone calls was from a woman who said, "Dr. Turpin, my name is Maurine Clark. I'm a registered nurse. I've read about you and seen your picture in the newspapers. Do you have your license yet?"

"No, but I'm expecting it in a month or so."

We talked about the problems of getting a medical license in Hong Kong, then Mrs. Clark said, "I've heard that you want to start a medical facility in the Walled City. Have you found a place there?"

"Not yet."

"I'd like to show you a little child-care center we started two years ago," she said. "We get milk and wafers from Church World Service and feed about seventy-five children a day there. We also have clinic days when we see perhaps forty patients. If we could offer the services of a licensed physician we could treat many more. Will you look at it?"

"The sooner the better," I said.

The oldest of the solemn-faced children who went to the child-care center in the Walled City were only ten or eleven, and few were alone. Almost all had younger brothers and sisters with them, some infants strapped to backs papoose style. Except for their Oriental appearance, these kids could have come right out of Casa de Todos. Some looked healthy enough, others obviously suffered from the malnutrition, skin lesions, and respiratory disorders typical of underprivileged children everywhere.

When all had been fed Maurine asked, "Well, what do you think?"

"I think it's too bad I don't have my license and can't start working with these children right away," I said.

"Then you'll join us?"

"Of course."

That was the beginning of Project Concern's clinic work in the Walled City. In the meantime, shaken by the disaster of Typhoon Wanda, which hit two days after our arrival in Hong Kong, I was anxious to open a clinic on the water as soon as possible. Pelted by the driving rain, I had stood with Paul and Dennis beside a shelter watching the typhoon in action. It killed one hundred and fifty-eight people, injured over six hundred more, and left about five thousand boat people homeless. It also left me with the searing memory of a child grabbing one of my legs and quickly slipping away when he realized from the texture of my Western trousers that I was not his father. I thought of the little Mexican boy at Casa de Todos who had held me in the same way when Mollie and I brought food and toys and medicine there for the first time. The Mexican boy was lucky. At least he knew where to find his parents.

The typhoon killed any chance of getting an early start on a floating clinic, for all the shipyards were tied up with repair jobs. While asking everyone they met to keep an eye open for a junk that might be converted into a clinic, Paul and Dennis had their hands full with other problems, not the least of which was storage space. We had no idea we would need so much, picturing only comparatively small loads coming via Operation Handclasp. Instead, there were huge shipments—one Navy APA brought us twenty-four tons—and it was essential we get something near the water front. As usual, for from his Hong Kong days he had hundreds of contacts, Dennis found the answer. Through one of his friends he arranged for Paul to meet Mr. Lum, owner of the Chipwau flashlight factory, who had just built an eight-story godown (warehouse) that included two floors of cold-storage space. He let us have the entire sixth floor free for a year and whatever cold-storage space we might need at a discount.

Paul's old service connections came in very handy. The movements of United States Navy ships in and out of Hong Kong were confidential until a few days before actual arrival, then there would be a scramble for lighters and longshoremen. Whenever a ship with Project Concern supplies was due in, somebody would tip Paul off far enough in advance for him to arrange for proper unloading.

While we appreciated all contributions, some of the things that arrived were startling. When Paul, Dennis, and I went down to unpack our first Operation Handclasp shipment, one item was a badly bent colander. The same shipment brought a pair of Little League baseball shin guards, a set of football pads, and an old dental washbasin. I still have a picture of myself wearing the shin guards and the pads, and peering over the washbasin with the colander on my head. Once, while sorting drugs, Shirley came across a bottle of horse liniment. Another time we received eight thousand cases of Gerber's baby food. We could use some, but eight thousand was a bit too much of a good thing. After calling a few other relief agencies, Paul and Shirley delivered three busloads to the Fanling Baby Home in the New Territories, north of Kowloon.

When I first heard about all the relief agencies in Hong Kong I wondered if they ever stepped on each other's toes, but after we got there I saw from our own experience how well they worked together. Our donation to the Fanling Baby Home was perfectly natural, since other agencies did so much for us. Church World Service, which helped back Maurine Clark's child-care center in the Walled City, was delighted to have us develop into it a Project Concern

71

clinic, and continued to donate food for the children. It also shared its godown at the Kowloon–Hong Kong wharf with whoever needed it. The Lutheran World Service, the Catholic Welfare Relief, the Christian Children's Fund, and Project Concern all were welcome to use it, moving supplies in and out at will. Every relief agency in Hong Kong was just as generous, just as willing to help other organizations.

Until our stateside drug-sorting system was perfected, this job had to be handled at 25 Oxford Road. Everyone, even the children, pitched in, since it was impossible for one person to do it all. Shirley, who knew something about the pharmaceutical companies and what they produced from her experience as my secretary in Coronado, took charge of the detail work. Sometimes there were drugs all over the downstairs floors, with squares marked off for each and everyone tiptoeing around to make sure nothing was disturbed. One misstep could nullify days of hard work. There were thousands of items, some precious, some useless, some spoiled by the time they reached us. As our pharmacist, Dennis had the final say on what to do with which drugs. Although many were thrown away, all had to be examined, a tiresome task that required rare patience.

One great source of satisfaction was the willing dedication of the people who wanted to work for us. The fact that we couldn't pay much meant nothing. This attitude was typified by Frank Hooper, the first person we hired in Hong Kong. A shy, homely-handsome, slightly stoop-shouldered Canadian veteran of the Korean War, with a long nose and horn-rimmed glasses, he rang the bell at Oxford Road one evening and asked for a job as a lab technician.

"We need a lab technician," I said, "but I don't think we can afford one."

"You can afford me," he said.

We took him on a two-weeks trial basis and when the

72

two weeks were up wondered how we had ever got along without him. There was nothing he couldn't or wouldn't do. He was a genius at being where he was most needed. He helped sort drugs, helped carry loads into the Walled City, helped feed the children there, even filled in as a nurse when we were shorthanded. The children who came to the clinic loved him, for he was a gentle humanitarian radiating such warmth that his inability to speak Chinese was no handicap. His was the universal language of compassion.

A restless soul before he came to us, Frank went home to Canada after Korea, worked as a lab technician, then started on a trip around the world. He got as far as Hong Kong, which he liked so much he took quarters in a house with an old family friend, Dorothy Plant. He decided to look for a job at just about the time we arrived. He has been with us ever since. Dorothy, a former writer and editor who organized the Canadian WRENS in World War II, joined us later and is now a full-time member of our Hong Kong staff.

One day Dr. Bob Worth, an American friend of ours, phoned and asked if we would take an unregistered woman refugee doctor recently arrived from the mainland. A delicately beautiful girl in her twenties, Peggy Chu became our second Hong Kong employee. Unlike most Chinese, who are very shy, Peggy was aggressive, eager to learn, and not a bit bashful about asking questions. The daughter of a manufacturer whose business had been taken over by the Communists, Peggy spoke guardedly of her past and scrupulously avoided publicity, for fear it would hurt her family. She was, in fact, so reluctant to talk about herself that we did not learn for months that she was engaged to a wealthy young Hong Kong jeweler. Although desperately poor, since she had left China with nothing, she would not marry him without a Western medical education, which she finally went to Canada to get.

Hong Kong was full of refugees like Peggy, mainland

73

Chinese doctors without licenses, in danger of forgetting everything they had ever learned because they could not practice. We took them both for our sake and theirs—it was good for us to have trained personnel and good for them to work in a hospital atmosphere. Soon after Peggy joined us, a missionary introduced us to Philip Cheung, a thin, painfully shy young man who, it turned out, was nearly starving. We hired him to work with Dennis as assistant pharmacist. One night a couple of months later we were all sitting around the living room in Oxford Road when Mollie happened to mention that we needed another nurse.

"I think I know one," Philip said.

"Who?" I asked.

He blushed, hung his head, and mumbled, "My wife."

It was the first we knew he was married. The next day Philip's wife, Amelia Wong (Chinese women retain their maiden names), joined us in the Walled City. Even shyer than Philip, she was so quiet that I thought for a long time she couldn't speak English. One day I asked Philip to get something, and Amelia told him where to find it. Not only did she understand English, she spoke it better than he did. I also soon discovered that she was the most efficient nurse I had ever seen. After some weeks of showing an unusual knowledge of her job, she finally admitted that she, too, was an unregistered doctor. She eventually met the Hong Kong medical requirements and now is one of our practicing physicians. Philip, who has had trouble satisfying the authorities there, became our pharmacist after Dennis went home, and still works in that capacity.

I shudder to think what would have happened to us without Dennis. One of the many things he did was help Paul find a boat for our floating clinic. A friend told him that Mr. Wong Wing Kit, one of several brothers who ran the Wing Cheung shipyards in Kowloon, might be able to get us a thirty-foot junk, which was about all we could afford. Mr. Wong knew someone who was trying to sell a sixty-three-foot lighter with a teakwood hull. A lighter, used for loading and transshipping around the harbor, has no power and must be towed, but that didn't matter, since we intended to anchor in one spot. This particular lighter was larger than anything we had in mind, and we shrank at the cost of rebuilding and refitting it. On the other hand, there was no question of its suitability, for it would provide ample space for a clinic.

After inspecting the hull, Andrew Lee, an architect with whom Dennis had gone to school, promised to help us lay out the floor plans. Paul suggested installing an apartment below decks for Mollie, the children, and me. That just about clinched our determination to buy it, because we knew we couldn't stay at 25 Oxford Road indefinitely. We then negotiated with the owner and agreed on a price of $15,000 H.K. (about $2600 U.S.), more money than we had on hand, but not an impossible amount to raise.

After that, Paul, with much coaching from Dennis, began finding life one day of haggling after another. When Dennis went with him, there was no problem, but Paul often had to go alone. If the person he dealt with that day knew no English, Paul depended almost entirely on hand signals, smiles, eyebrow lifting, arm waving, and other gestures to make himself understood. Sketchy as it was, his Cantonese helped some, especially when it turned out to be better than the other man's English. I went along when I could and, although I had nothing to contribute to the conversation, I rarely came away without learning something.

Chinese merchants do most of their business over tea, which they call *yum cha*. One day Paul had a *yum cha* date with two men from whom he was trying to buy some equipment for the boat. As they talked the *foky* (waiter) refilled their teacups and the two merchants tapped their fingertips on the table. They did this each time their cups were refilled. This was how they thanked the *foky*, a throwback to the old days when such service drew a kowtow, requiring the recipient to go to his knees and say, "Thank you, and I hope I have the opportunity to do something for you." Custom through the centuries had first cut this awkward expression of gratitude down to rapping the knuckles —which, if you have a good imagination, look like knees— on the table, and, finally, to tapping fingertips.

When Paul wanted to buy anything for the boat, which was being refitted at the Wing Chung yards, he never went alone, but with one of Wong Wing Kit's assistants, a man named Mr. Leung. Mr. Leung, who almost always had a big smile on his face, was a sort of go-between between the shipyard and the merchants. His English was about as good as Paul's Cantonese, which consisted of *"gei dou chin a?"* meaning "how much?" and *"tai gwai,"* meaning "too expensive." About all Mr. Leung knew was "too much," "not too much," and "good price."

One day they went out to buy four-by-eight plywood sheets for some of the bulkhead partitions on the main deck. During *yum cha* Mr. Leung indicated that the price would be fourteen Hong Kong dollars a sheet. This was something less than three dollars United States, since an American dollar was worth five dollars and seventy cents Hong Kong.

"Tai Gwai," said Paul.

"Not too much," said Mr. Leung.

"Tai Gwai," said Paul.

"Good price," said Mr. Leung.

He grinned. Paul grinned. The merchant grinned. Then Mr. Leung said, *"Geidou chin a?"*

Paul held up eight fingers, and everybody laughed. The *foky* poured some tea, and they all tapped their fingertips on the table and went on bargaining. They finally settled for eleven dollars Hong Kong a sheet.

Sometimes they parted without coming to any agreement, and Paul and Mr. Leung would walk away. Invariably, the merchant would go to the shipyard the next day with a better offer and everyone would return to the tea-house to talk things over.

Whenever they arrived at a deal, Mr. Leung and the merchant continued to talk for some time. Paul thought nothing of it until one day, after saying good-bye, Mr. Leung suddenly went back for a last word with a man who had just sold them some equipment.

"What was that all about?" Paul asked Dennis, who had gone with him.

"Tea money," Dennis said.

"What's tea money?"

"A little something for the merchants," Dennis told him. "Sort of a kickback."

Tea money went with every transaction, no matter how small. Sometimes it amounted to less than a penny in United States money.

Although the merchants haggled over everything, after they closed a deal they stuck to it. However, they some-times made infuriating mistakes, once causing Paul Fleener and Frank Hooper, who are among the mildest-mannered men I know, to blow their stacks on the very same after-noon. Frank, who rarely asked for anything, had one simple request for his laboratory. "Please," he told Dennis, who was on his way to see the merchants, "don't get me stainless-steel basins. I use dyes in my tests, so be sure they're porce-lain." When Dennis returned to Oxford Road that night he assured Frank the sinks would be porcelain. Just to check, Frank went down to the boat the day they were being installed. They were stainless steel. Frank hit the roof. He got porcelain ones.

At just about the same time Paul, who had repeatedly insisted on plain plywood walls for the staff lounge, walked in to find them already half covered with formica topping, exactly what he didn't want. When he failed to convince the foreman to remove the formica, he drove to the ship-yard and made Wong Wing Kit go back to the boat with

77

him. I guess the poor man didn't dare not go. Paul stands six feet three, and every inch was bristling with anger. His performance saved us a small fortune, since the formica cost twenty-eight Hong Kong dollars a sheet and the plywood six.

At Thanksgiving Mollie and Shirley prepared a turkey dinner with all the trimmings, including cranberry sauce, dressing, gravy, mashed potatoes, a green bean dish, and both mincemeat and pumpkin pies. We invited our four Chinese-language teachers, only one of whom had ever had a Western-style meal before. The other three stared in obvious dismay at the silverware. We showed them how to use their knives, forks, and spoons, but I suppose this is a skill that isn't learned at one sitting. After vainly trying to manipulate his utensils for fifteen or twenty minutes, one of the teachers suddenly blurted out, "Don't you have any chopsticks in the house?" When we produced chopsticks, all four, including the one who knew how to handle our silverware, picked them up and began eating. It was the only time I ever saw anyone polish off mashed potatoes, gravy, cranberry sauce, and even pumpkin pie with chopsticks.

We had dessert to the tune of a clanging Oriental arrangement of "When the Saints Go Marching In" and "In the Sweet Bye and Bye," played by a white-jacketed marching band out on the street. The musicians were leading a Buddhist funeral.

CHAPTER

8

The World Congress of the Junior Chamber of Commerce International met at the Ambassador Hotel in Hong Kong in November, 1962. Doug Blankenship, the national president, was an old friend of mine from Atlanta. Mollie and I had known him and his wife, Katie, when I was assistant pastor to Reverend Bob Kerr at the College Park Methodist Church, to which the Blankenships belonged. When I visited Doug at his home during the promotion trip following my return from Hong Kong, he was deeply interested in Project Concern. One day I had a letter from him at Oxford Road telling me he intended to nominate me as one of the Ten Outstanding Young Men of the Year, who are named annually by the Jaycees of America. He enclosed an application for me, but with all the things that demanded my attention, I didn't do anything about it. Just before the deadline, Mollie rescued it from Jan, who was marking it all up with her crayons, and told me to fill it out and send it to Doug. By then I had forgotten what it was, but I filled in the blanks and signed it. Some weeks later I had a short note from Doug saying he had received it and sent it to the judges. A few weeks after that he wrote again, inviting Mollie and me to the opening session of the World Congress. When he and Katie arrived in Hong Kong, we went to see them at the hotel.

"Jim," Doug said, "I've got some good news for you. You've been named one of our Ten Outstanding Young Men for 1962, and we want you to attend the award ceremonies in Little Rock in January."

"How could I have been chosen?" I said. "We're just getting started."

"You've already done enough to impress the judges," he

said. "The idea of Project Concern is sound. It's practical and humanitarian, and it creates tremendous good will for us overseas."

While truly thrilled, I honestly didn't think I deserved the honor. We had been in Hong Kong less than four months. All we had done was operate a small clinic for a few weeks in the Walled City. All we owned was a modest bank account and title to a boat hull we hadn't paid for. Project Concern was off to a fine start, but it was still only a start.

As one of the year's Ten Outstanding Young Men, I was in excellent company. Among the other nine named by the Jaycees in 1962 were Congressman John Brademas of Indiana, co-author of the Peace Corps bill, Dr. James Jude, who developed the closed-chest heart resuscitation method, Berl Bernhard, head of the Civil Rights Commission, and Curtiss Anderson, editor of a major national magazine. Only a few weeks short of my thirty-fifth birthday, I just got in under the wire, since that is the TOYM age limit.

As Mollie and I drove home that night, I said, "I'm afraid they've made another mistake."

"What do you mean?" she said.

"Billie Sol Estes was a previous winner. That was the first mistake. I'm the second."

"John F. Kennedy was a previous winner, too," she retorted. "Anyhow, mistake or no mistake, this will be the making of Project Concern."

She was quite right. My election opened a flood of dynamic new contacts, for it began a close relationship between us and the Jaycees which still flourishes. It enabled us to make friends in places we had never been and never would have thought of going. It resulted not only in financial advantages but gave us the services of scores of fine young people from all over the world who might otherwise never have heard of us. To this day there are Jaycees or

80

friends of Jaycees working either as paid employees or as volunteers for Project Concern.

By the time Mollie and I arrived in Los Angeles on our way to the TOYM award ceremonies, Ed Flynn had an itinerary arranged which would take me all over the country. It was, of course, a golden opportunity to capitalize on the international publicity set off by the award.

We first went to Little Rock for ceremonies presided over by an earlier TOYM winner, Reverend Bob Richards, the former world's pole-vault champion. My parents came out from Ashland, and many of our friends from various parts of the Middle West were also there. With a few stops en route, we then went to New York for television and radio appearances and a series of press conferences, including one at the Overseas Press Club. Berl Bernhard invited us to a White House civil-rights reception, after which I planned to continue on South. Since the reception was a week off, Mollie, who felt she had already been away from the children too long, went back to Hong Kong. I worked around New York, then flew to Washington with Ann and Curt Anderson.

I had hoped to meet President Kennedy, but there were six hundred people at the reception, and it was obvious that he couldn't greet us all individually. Curt introduced me to Senator Hubert Humphrey, then to Vice-President Lyndon B. Johnson and Mrs. Johnson. The Vice-President was engrossed in a lengthy conversation with other officials, but Lady Bird listened carefully as Curt began telling her about me and Project Concern. After a while, her eyes big as saucers, she tugged on her husband's sleeve and said, "Lyndon, Lyndon, come on and hear what this boy is doing in Hong Kong." The Vice-President turned and smiled, then turned back to the others and resumed the discussion which had commanded his attention.

Disappointed at not having met President Kennedy, I was standing in a doorway apart from the crowd talking to Ann Anderson when I became aware of someone trying gently to push through. Absorbed in my own conversation, I paid no attention until I felt the pressure again. That time I turned to find the President patiently waiting for me to move out of his way.

"I'm Jim Turpin, from Hong Kong, Mr. President," I stammered. Then, as we shook hands, I managed to add, "I'm in the TOYM group. We're honored to be here."

"We're honored to have you," he said.

When I introduced him to Ann, they talked a moment about an article on the Kennedy family that had appeared in Curt's publication. Before turning to leave, he said, "We'll talk again, Mrs. Anderson. Your husband is a respected journalist." Then he smiled at me, said, "Good luck in your work, Dr. Turpin," and disappeared.

"He addressed me as 'Doctor,' " I said. "He knew who I was."

"You would be surprised at the number of people who know who you are, Jim," Ann said.

I thought of that when, soon after my return to Hong Kong, I had a letter from Michael Burke, inviting me on an all-expense tour of Australian Jaycee groups to talk about Project Concern. Mike, a member of the Ballarat, Victoria, Jaycees, had been through the Walled City and the Yaumati shelter with us during the World Congress, but had said so little that I had no idea our work had impressed him particularly. The tour he arranged began at Perth, where I was amazed to find twenty-five Jaycees waiting for me at one-thirty in the morning, waving a huge banner that read, "Welcome, Jim Turpin." Even at that hour there was television coverage, with more the next day when I appeared at half a dozen functions. The Perth newspapers had Project Concern on page one, and people actually stopped me on the street, recognizing me from press and television pictures.

Then I flew to Adelaide on Anset Airlines, courtesy of

Reginald Anset, who provided my transportation all over Australia. In Adelaide a reception committee of about seventy-five greeted me with a banner which said, "Adelaide Welcomes Project Concern," and once again I had a full schedule of appearances and speeches. It was too much. On my second day in Adelaide I began to feel rocky going to a TV studio. The next thing I knew I had a full-blown attack of angioneurotic edema, which comes on within thirty minutes. When my eyes swelled up in the studio I had to cancel that appearance and go to bed. I rested thirty-six hours before I was well enough to continue on to Melbourne.

Mike Burke was in the group scheduled to meet me there, since Ballarat is only about fifty miles to the north. The Melbourne airport was fogged in and the plane landed at another one twenty-five or thirty miles away. Again to my amazement, I was met by Mike and the rest of the reception committee which formed a motorcade for a triumphant drive back to Melbourne. The boys there, aware of my illness in Adelaide, had arranged a less strenuous, but no less impressive, schedule. I had fewer affairs to attend and fewer speeches to make, but the crowds were big, and the response to a television appearance terrific.

It was that way all over Australia and New Zealand—in Sydney, in Brisbane, in Hobart, in Canberra, in Wellington, in Invercargill, and in intermediate spots where Jaycee groups asked to meet me. On the way back to Perth I stopped in Adelaide again to make up for the lost hours there. That time I went through with an appearance on the same television show I had missed when I got sick.

I have not returned to Australia or New Zealand since, but I look forward to more trips there in the future, although nothing will ever be like that first one. It taught me that Project Concern had the same appeal to the young people of a foreign country that it had to the young people of my own. And, of course, no other trip—either there or anywhere else—will ever provide exactly the same thrills of surprise and satisfaction. That was the first time I found myself the center of attention in a land I had never seen before.

The most important result of the trip was the response, human and financial. We had about three hundred applications from people there who wanted to serve Project Concern. To this day many Australians work with us, several back on second tours of duty. We have also received thousands of dollars, much of the money in regular monthly contributions, from our Australian friends. This type of commitment is of special value for budgeting purposes.

We owe a great deal to the Jaycees, more than I can ever fully express. Mollie was completely right. Our alliance with them, through my selection as one of the Ten Outstanding Young Men of 1962, was indeed the making of Project Concern.

CHAPTER

9

We called the boat the *Yauh Oi*, which is Cantonese for "brotherly love." She was a beautiful craft, with a hull of very dark blue and a superstructure of gleaming white. On one side was our blue-and-white emblem and "Yauh Oi Brotherly Love" spelled out, on the other the words "Project Concern" in English and in Cantonese. The top deck, shaded in the middle by a canvas cover, was flat, to be used as a play area for the children and an overflow waiting room. The main deck had a registration and waiting room, an examining room, a clinic, a staff lounge, a pharmacy, and a laboratory. Below decks were our living quarters, cramped but complete, with a big open area in the center. On each side of the *Yauh Oi* were two sets of doors leading to the water, making it easily accessible to any craft that pulled alongside.

The launching spanned three days. For the convenience of dignitaries who had agreed to come, we had scheduled it in advance for Saturday, March 9, 1963, but the boat wasn't quite ready then. After the ceremonies, she was towed back to the Wing Chung yards where the fittings were completed, then taken to her permanent anchorage the following Monday.

Everyone on the staff—we had fifteen people by then—appeared at the yard to help put on the finishing touches the day before the launching. We worked all day and well into the night polishing and waxing floors and hardware until the boat was as shiny inside as out. Gifts from friends had been pouring in all week—floral arrangements, multi-colored lanterns, ribbons, and pennants. Several Kaifong Chinese fraternal organizations gave us mirrors, the nicest gifts the Chinese can send, for they believe mirrors bring good luck. We have ours hanging all over the boat. A tremendous white banner with gold Chinese characters saying, "May the gods bless you," arrived on the day before the launching. The Lum family sent a dozen bamboo chairs for the roof furniture, and bouquets of flowers. A long string of firecrackers, to be set off at the ribbon cutting that opened the ceremonies, was draped over the *Yauh Oi*'s bow, while crisscrossing the boat were the colorful international signal pennants, the gift of Wong Wing Kit.

At dawn on March 9 a tug towed the *Yauh Oi* from the shipyard to the main pier of the Hong Kong and Kowloon Wharf Company, two and a half hours away. Most of this trip was in what is known as Central Avenue, a water channel about seventy-five feet wide. All along the way we were greeted by cheering, waving boat people. The pier was already crowded when we arrived, and when it was time to cut the ribbon, the whole area was packed.

Kwok Yim Tsun, a small girl who lived in the shelter, cut the ribbon, Keith set off the string of firecrackers and everybody cheered. Several officials spoke briefly. Marshall Green, the United States consul, told us the American people were proud of us and that we were bringing honor to our government. Lin You Bor, of the Hong Kong Urban Council, welcomed us on behalf of the Chinese community and thanked us for opening such a badly-needed medical facility. It was thrilling and touching and a great source of satisfaction to us all.

Two days later, when the last of the fittings had been installed, we went aboard the *Yauh Oi* to ride along Central Avenue to our permanent anchorage beside the marriage boat in the heart of the Yaumati shelter. The trip out was uneventful, but when we arrived we nearly created our own first patients because of wind gusts. At the anchorage, the towboat had to loosen its hold to get us into position to be moved sideways out of Central Avenue. Caught by the wind, we began drifting across the channel toward the small junks and sampans on the other side, then gathered speed while the tug crew tried desperately to refasten the towline. Suddenly aware of the danger, people in front of us ran in all directions, leaping from boat to boat to get out of the way. For a harrowing few seconds it appeared that the *Yauh Oi*, a monster compared to the craft she was headed for, would crush everything in her path. Only fast work on the part of the tug crew, which finally got us harnessed before we did any damage, prevented a serious accident.

While we continued to live at Oxford Road until our below-decks apartment was completed, we were able to open the clinic on the afternoon of March 12, the day after we anchored. We charged fifty cents Hong Kong (about eight and a half cents United States) for registration to

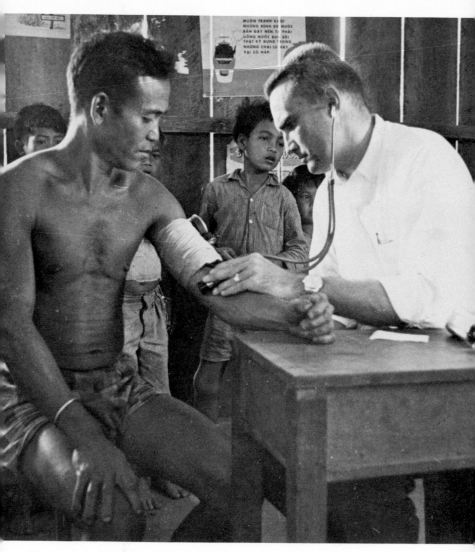

He wears the bracelet of the Montagnard *tribe of* KoHo, *of which* Dr. Turpin *has been made a brother and given the name Bacsi Hakkah—* "Doctor who remembers us."

Dr. Turpin with his first class of recruits for the Village Medical Assistants *training program in 1964. To date more than fifty young people have been trained under a joint program of Project Concern's hospital at DaMpao and the provincial hospital at Dalat.*

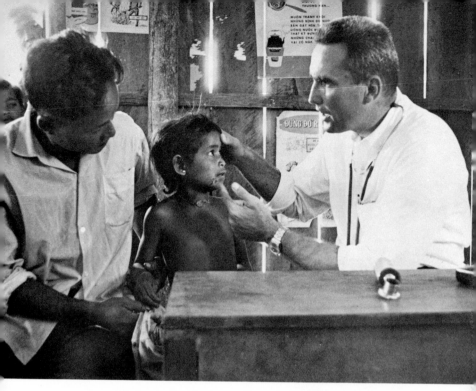

Dr. Turpin winning the confidence of a little Montagnarde,
Outpatient clinic, hospital at DaMpao, Vietnam.

Elderly women in the waiting room at DaMpao, Vietnam.

Dr. Turpin (right) with H'Klas (center), a young Montagnard assistant, making a routine visit to one of the villages in the area of Project Concern's hospital at DaMpao.

Villagers waiting to see the doctor inside.

On village visits, it is important that the people watch procedures and listen to instructions as the Village Medical Assistant *translates them for the patient. K'Moung, at right, reads a thermometer.*

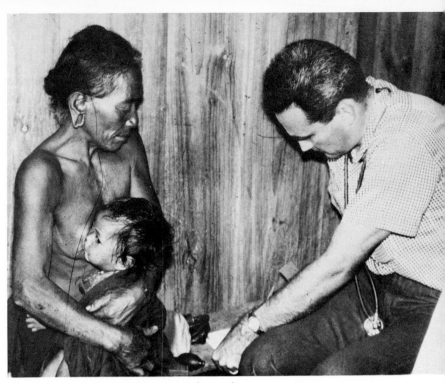

A worried Montagnarde *mother.*

Village Medical Assistant, *serving a fellow* Montagnard *tribesman in his own language and traditions.*

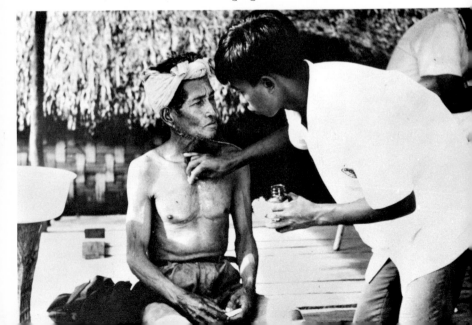

A village elder.

Little KoHo *in the basket, with* **Dr. Turpin** *and* **Frank Hopper.**

Montagnard *children living in the Central Highlands of Vietnam.*

Montagnards *guarding the strategic hamlet against the Viet Cong. Dr. Turpin and H'Doi at right.*

Target practice in a mountain village, central Vietnam. Dr. Turpin, aiming. Dr. Frank Hui, student Village Medical Assistants, *and Montagnard soldier.*

Water buffaloes are sometimes offered in ritual animal sacrifice.

James Wesley Turpin, M.D.

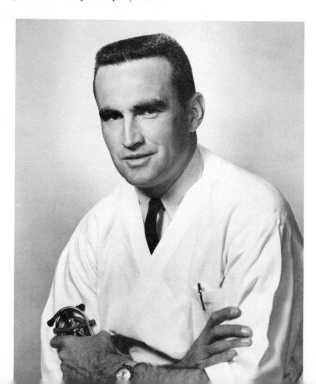

Squatters' shacks, about 300,000 of which cling precariously to the hillsides of Hong Kong and Kowloon.

Dark, narrow street outside Project Concern's clinic in the Walled City, Kowloon. Children bringing still smaller ones to be seen by the doctor.

In the Walled City Kowloon clinic.

Dr. Turpin and friend.

On a twenty-foot boat a family of six or ten will make its home. In the stormy season sampans huddle together by the thousands. Project Concern's two floating clinics, Yauh Oi and Ming Ling, offer medical, minor surgical, EENT, dental, and X-ray services to the 32,000 boat people of Yaumati Typhoon Shelter.

Scott Turpin learning to scull.

Paying the daily call on Wong Fat.

those who could afford it, not for what the money would mean to us, but for what it would mean to them. It would preserve their dignity and pride as well as remind them that the drugs and services they received were not worthless. We took the money only the first time we saw a patient, charging nothing for subsequent visits. One payment made the point; more would cause hardship. Since everyone wanted to pay, only the utterly destitute didn't.

Besides those who had joined us before the *Yauh Oi* clinic opened, we had two additional doctors, Dr. Tony Tse and a young American naval officer, Dr. Fred Sabotka, from upstate New York. Fred, on a month's leave from his duty station at a navy dispensary in Taiwan, had read about us in *Stars and Stripes*, and rang our bell at Oxford Road a few nights before the *Yauh Oi* was launched. He spent his entire leave with us and came back a year later. He also opened a clinic for the poverty-stricken mountain people of Taiwan, where he worked in his spare time.

Our first patient was a sixteen-year-old girl named Lee Mui. With only five grams of hemoglobin in her blood, a third the normal amount, she suffered from iron-deficiency anemia. The only previous treatment she had had was by an herb doctor. When he failed to help her, she had undergone an ancient and painful Chinese needle treatment. We gave her vitamins with iron, and she gradually improved.

On that first day I had to go aboard a sampan to examine a patient too weak to move. She was Ho Yuen See, an eleven-year-old girl with a temperature of 104. The child was so badly dehydrated she had not been able to walk for ten days. Her sister told us they had given her herbs and an old, cruelly uncomfortable pinching treatment to "bring out the pain." She responded so well to antibiotics that she came aboard the *Yauh Oi* under her own power on her next visit the following day.

The diseases we saw on the boat were much the same

as those in the Walled City—pulmonary, skin and bone tuberculosis, parasitic ailments of the skin and intestinal tract, trachoma, bronchial diseases, and scabies. Occasionally we found an opium addict and once in a while a cholera case. However, there wasn't so much cholera in the typhoon shelter as in the Walled City, probably because there wasn't quite so much filth.

The boat people are far more superstitious. The older ones think it's bad luck to go ashore. The Buddhists among them worship a goddess of the sea who they believe takes care of them only if they stay on the sea. Some actually are sick at the thought of touching dry land, just as some land people have aquaphobia, a deep-seated fear of the water.

One of the oddest superstitions of the boat people is their refusal to turn a fish over after it's been cooked. This applies to their guests as well as to themselves. Whenever having a meal aboard a junk or sampan, you must dig the meat of a fish out between the bones from the upper side, for your hosts believe if you turn the fish over their boat will turn over.

The principal difference between Hong Kong boat people and land people is in shopping. On land people go to shops; on the water the shops go to the people. There are meat boats and vegetable boats and grocery boats. There is a repair boat, a painting boat, and a supply boat. There are cookie, soft-drink, salt, fish, sugar-cane and ice boats. There is even a boat with a blind masseuse. Every other day the water boat comes around.

Besides our clinic, one of the few service boats that remain in the same place is our next-door neighbor, the marriage boat. This gay, colorful junk about the size of the *Yauh Oi* is used not only for marriages, but for celebrations of all kinds. A fascinating Yaumati establishment, the marriage boat is the center of much of the shelter's social life. Chinese weddings are usually two-day affairs, attended by relatives from outside the shelter as well as in, some coming from as far away as Chung Chow, a fishing island twelve miles out to sea. The people come in their own gaily-colored junks or sampans, and stay until the festivities, complete with clanging and drum-beating and dragon dances and firecracker-popping and banqueting and partying and singing, are over.

One of the hazards of getting out to the *Yauh Oi* is the duck market, which you must cross to reach the nearest pier. This is a fantastic, unbelievably dirty area, with thousands of quacking ducks and chickens and all manner of garbage—old shoes, orange peels, eggshells, fruit pits, bloody duck heads and entrails—in the street. The odors are overpowering, the slime so deep it nearly covers your shoes, and the footing so treacherous you have to watch your step every minute. One of our volunteers, Hedy Wong, slipped and fell headlong in the dirtiest part of the duck market, and we didn't see her for a week. She told Dorothy Plant later it took her that long to get rid of the smell.

Without an auxiliary boat of our own in the first few months of the floating clinic, we went back and forth in sampan taxis, operated by women or children who poled them from the rear with single oars. Our favorite was Ah Tai, a tiny woman with six gold teeth in front, which she exhibited in a huge smile that rarely left her face. Although she led a hard life—she had several children and maybe a husband to support—she seemed to enjoy every minute of it. She attached herself to us the first week we were in the shelter, waiting at the pier for people to go to the *Yauh Oi*, then hanging around there for passengers back to the shore. Since there was always somebody going one way or the other, this suited everyone very well. Ah Tai could make a living, and she saved us from having to look for transportation whenever we wanted to leave the boat.

In the beginning she collected fifty cents a ride (about a dime United States) from each of us, but Dennis Wong soon put a stop to that. He gave her twenty cents one morning after she took him and Paul to the boat.

"Dennis," Paul said, "I've always given Ah Tai fifty cents."

"That's too much," Dennis said.

He gave Ah Tai a stern lecture, which she took with her toothy grin, then turned back to Paul and said, "We use the economic principle of *yut hogee*—one dime for one person. Unless you have a heavy load, never pay more."

Eventually we hired Ah Tai for seventeen U.S. dollars a month, about seven American dollars more than she could make on her own. She is still on our staff, entertaining everyone who goes to the *Yauh Oi* with her smile and her chatter and, to the best of my knowledge, scrupulously refusing so much as a penny tip.

One day Ah Tai, who rarely came aboard the clinic, rushed up the steps and charged past Jonathan Wong, our registrar, yelling, *"Dopun yee sung—fidee—fidee"* ("Dr. Turpin—hurry—hurry"). When Jonathan, always careful to see that everyone other than emergency cases wait his turn, caught up with her, she told him a lady in a sampan was so close to having a baby there wasn't time to bring her aboard. Amelia and I dropped everything and ran, just in time to ease a mother's delivery of her sixth child.

Every so often Mary Su came aboard, usually with someone who needed help and was too shy to come alone to get it. She hires crews made up mostly of women to paint Navy ships that come into the harbor, in return for which she gets all the garbage. She has her business down to a science. As soon as they are permitted on board, her women go into the mess halls to separate the food as the men scrape their plates. Mary Su made such a good living selling garbage around the typhoon shelters that she has sent four adopted children through college, although she is herself illiterate.

One day a young fellow unable to walk was carried

aboard the *Yauh Oi*. A native of Canton, he was one of the few people I met with an exit visa from the communist Chinese to come to Hong Kong for medical care. From what I could gather, they were willing to let him out temporarily for two reasons—as a cripple, he was considered a detriment to their society, and as a Cantonese with his whole family still on the mainland, he was unlikely to say anything against the Red regime.

He suffered from a central nervous system defect the exact nature of which I couldn't determine in the short time he was allowed to stay in Hong Kong. His lower extremities were paralyzed but, with no history that sounded like polio, his ailment probably was congenital. If in the colony long enough we could have arranged for him to have extensive X-rays and diagnostic treatment at Queen Mary's Hospital, but there wasn't much we could do for him. When I explained the situation in detail, he smiled amiably, and warmly shook hands as he said good-bye. I learned that he was flattered and impressed by the personal attention we gave him. Nobody had ever before shown anywhere nearly so much interest in him, and he appreciated ours, even though we couldn't help him.

Wong Fat, a little old man with soft brown eyes and a wistful smile, practically became a member of the family. We first saw him when he tottered aboard one afternoon, wheezing from the efforts of poling his tiny sampan to the *Yauh Oi* and obviously suffering from a variety of ailments. When one of the girls asked why he had come alone, he replied that it was the only way he could get there. His family, waiting for him to die, neglected him so badly they hadn't even bothered to see that he was fed. With emphysema, malnutrition, and high blood pressure, he belonged in a hospital, but even if I could have found one to take him I'm sure he wouldn't have gone. He had spent his long life on the water and intended to die there.

When he asked if he could stay with us, we let him tie

his sampan to one of our floats, and he became our lone hospital patient. Every day we fed him, gave him his digitalis and diuretics, and checked his lungs and blood pressure. Pretty soon he was well enough to come aboard for treatment, but he still refused to go back to his family. He kept his sampan tied to our float until the day he died in 1965, content in the knowledge that the last two years had been the happiest of his life.

Most Chinese families, unlike Wong Fat's, are very solicitous of their elderly. One day the biggest junk ever to visit us tied up at the patient's float, and a young man told Jonathan Wong they had traveled four hours from an island near the Chinese mainland to see if we could help his ailing grandfather. Since the old man was too weak and in too much pain to be brought aboard, Amelia and I went out to see him. The whole family—twenty-one people—stood around during the examination, which revealed evidence of anemia and severe acute arthritis.

When we were finished I said, "If I make him better quickly, I want to go on a fishing trip with you someday."

They all grinned, some laughing aloud, and assured me it was a bargain. We gave the sick man cortisone and intravenous iron. A month later they brought him back much improved. They wanted to take me out with them then, but I didn't have time. Some weeks later I did go, spending a wonderful day on that big junk and somehow managing to down the baby octopus these grateful people pressed on me. They were so happy for the chance to pay me in the only way they could that I didn't have the heart to tell them I wasn't used to baby octopus for lunch or any other meal.

Not so satisfying was the unhappy experience I had with a slender, pale refugee mother who came in one day with a tiny baby wrapped in a dirty rag of a blanket. The infant, a beautiful little girl, had a cough, but wasn't seriously sick. She lay across my lap, a lovely little bundle of humanity, while Amelia and I examined her as the mother sat close by.

"You have a very pretty baby," I said to the mother, through Amelia.

Unsmiling, the mother stared at me, then said, *"Yiu m'yui a?"*

"What did she say, Amelia?"

" 'Do you want it?' " Amelia repeated.

"She doesn't mean it, does she?"

"Yes, Doctor," Amelia said. "She means it. To her, an infant girl, no matter how pretty, is just one more mouth to feed."

For a moment, I actually felt physically sick. I sighed deeply, swallowed, then very gently picked the baby up and handed her back to the mother. I wanted to say, "Hold it close," to yell, "Love it," to shriek, "Give it affection," but the words wouldn't come out. While waiting for the medicine, the woman held the child indifferently, then left without even looking down at her.

At thirty-five Wong Wai Mun, his eyes cloudy and his senses dulled from twenty years on opium, seemed an old, broken, defeated man when he first came aboard the *Yauh Oi.* He wept when I put a hand on his shoulder and smiled at him, for everyone else he had gone to for help had reproached him. Thanks to his own intense desire and the cooperation of his family, we got him to break the habit. Now he brings in friends with similar problems, in itself the best therapy he could have.

Although we had good luck with Wong Wai Mun, we find it as hard to cure drug addicts as does everyone else who tries. One father of eight, who for twelve years spent three-quarters of his pay on heroin, came to us a few months after we opened the floating clinic. Despite his own efforts and whatever we tried to do, he is still "chasing the dragon," and I doubt if he'll ever stop. In Hong Kong, addicts take heroin, an opium derivative, just as they do opium itself—by inhaling the smoke. They place the drug on a piece of aluminum foil and heat it from underneath, then draw the smoke into their lungs through a soda straw as it swirls about on the foil.

As word of Project Concern spread in the United States and abroad, more and more people asked to work with us. We had volunteers from the Orient, from Australia and New Zealand, and, especially during the summer, when there were school and college vacations, from Canada and the States. One of our favorites during our first summer in Yaumati was Hazel Hunt, redheaded principal of a school for the mentally retarded in Jersey City. Warm, casual, friendly, she endeared herself to us all. A fisherman's small daughter, suffering ringworm of the scalp, was so insistent that only Hazel dress her scalp lesions every day that we called the child "Hazel's head."

Two Stanford students, Marsden Blois of Atherton, California, and Nettleton Paine of Indian Wells, Kansas, spent the summer of 1963 with us, packing pills, organizing children's parties, arranging with local businessmen to donate money for refreshments and movie cartoons, and helping wherever they could in the Walled City and the typhoon shelter. Karen Fok, a Chinese medical student at Columbia, worked with us that summer, as did Collin Kwok, a senior medical student at California, and Mary Hatt, a social-science supervisor from South Bend, Indiana. Others came for shorter periods, many returning in subsequent years.

The more people we had the more patients we could handle. Before the summer ended, over one hundred and fifty were appearing at the *Yauh Oi* every day. Unless we could expand we would have to turn people away. The *Yauh Oi*, which had seemed so spacious in March, was obviously too small by August. One difficulty was our lack of X-ray, dental, and on-the-spot storage facilities. We also needed an eye, ear, nose and throat department.

I announced our needs in our monthly newsletter, which

went to our supporters, including Jaycee groups everywhere. Within a few weeks, the New Zealand Jaycees voted to raise $8,000 toward the purchase of an auxiliary boat to be anchored beside the *Yauh Oi*. Supplementing this gift, the Kowloon Rotary Club West voted in September, 1963, to raise $14,000 United States to complete the project.

When the new boat, the *Ming Ling*, was hauled along Central Avenue for the ribbon-cutting ceremony at the pier, a man on a work junk we passed bowed to me and said over and over, "Thank you—thank you—thank you." Others heard him and also called out along the way. By the time we arrived, I was so choked up I had to get a good grip on myself before I could speak. The ribbon-cutting ceremony was much like the one that launched the *Yauh Oi*. Several local dignitaries took part as did two distinguished guests from overseas, Carl Miller, president of Rotary International, and Peter Perry, president of the Australian Jaycees. The proudest participant of all was the representative of the Yaumati shelter—Wong Fat.

With United States Navy ships constantly coming and going, we got to know many of the personnel. One day I was invited aboard the aircraft carrier *Hancock*, which had earned the nickname *Fighting Hannah* in World War II. The captain of the carrier, just back from two months on maneuvers, welcomed me on the flight deck, then presented me with a plastic model of a junk, to be built as a water ambulance for us. The officers and men of the *Hancock* had raised $2,800 for the purpose.

"What are you going to call it, Doctor?" asked the captain.

"The *Hancock* is the *Fighting Hannah*," I said. "So we'll call this the *Helpful Hannah*."

The *Helpful Hannah* is a very handy little craft. Besides being equipped with resuscitation and emergency gear, it has an unloading boom, so we can use it as a lighter.

Most of the emergencies in the typhoon shelter were water accidents. People were always falling in, sometimes with tragic results, for an amazing number can't swim. Jan once spotted a strange-looking object in the water, which turned out to be a mother with a child strapped to her back, both dead. Two or three times people who had been told that we could perform miracles brought recently drowned loved ones to us, hoping we might somehow bring them back to life.

One of these victims was a child who had been dead for several hours. Her mother had gone to work, leaving her in the care of a slightly older brother, who was himself too young to know the difference between life and death. When the little girl fell into the water, the boy pulled her out, and told his mother what had happened when she arrived home. By then, of course, it was too late.

One day during a typhoon a crowded little junk tied up to us and the body of a man who had just died of a heart attack was brought aboard by two teenagers. They were the eldest of his nine children, all of whom had lived with him and their mother on the junk. The widow and children were not only grief-stricken, hungry, and soaked through, but in real danger because their boat was being badly blown about. We took them all aboard to wait out the typhoon. It lasted two days, during which we had a corpse in one of the examining rooms and ten terribly distraught survivors to house and feed. By scrounging around the *Yauh Oi*, Mollie dug up blankets and dry clothes, and used up all the rice and crackers aboard, as well as much of the tea. When the storm ended, the people thanked us, tenderly loaded the body into their junk, and poled off.

We were awakened in the middle of the night once by a barefooted Chinese woman motioning wildly that she had a sick child upstairs in the clinic. She came right into our apartment, which was easy enough since we never locked anything on the *Yauh Oi* but the pharmacy, where the drugs were kept. Mollie and I dressed and rushed up to find a child with a temperature of nearly 105. We sponged her and I gave her shots of fever depressant and an antibiotic. Then, suspecting meningitis, I wrote an emergency note and sent them to the nearest hospital. They were back the next day, for the hospital had refused to take them. Hong Kong hospitals are so terribly crowded they seldom have room for patients of doctors not on their staffs. I went ashore with the sick little girl and her mother, and that time the hospital admitted her.

An old woman with badly diseased kidneys was brought aboard one day. She had glomerulonephritis—her blood went through the renal tubes and kept them from sorting out the waste materials, which is their normal function. She became so anemic she needed transfusions. Although her family wanted to help, none would give blood, something most Chinese dislike doing. Frank Hooper volunteered, eventually donating five pints, which literally kept the woman alive. She was so grateful she gave him a set of chopsticks, the only thing she owned she considered of any value.

CHAPTER
10

Around the time we launched the *Ming Ling*, a Mr. Pang, short, fat, roly-poly, and greasy, came aboard the *Yauh Oi* to see me. I try not to jump to quick conclusions about people I find unattractive, but in this case it wasn't easy. Mr. Pang looked about as reliable as a weasel. He moved his hands nervously, his smile was a smirk, and his eyes were never still as he talked rapidly in fluent English he had learned as an automobile mechanic in San Francisco.

"Dr. Turpin," he said, "if you come with me I'll show you a place where ten thousand people live without money, food, or medical care."

"We want to help everyone we can," I said. "But between here and our clinic in the Walled City we have our hands full."

"This place is worse than here, worse than the Walled City," Mr. Pang said. "These people are refugees from Communist China with nowhere to go and no one to turn to. You've got to help them."

He talked on for half an hour, meeting each of my objections with a new argument, insisting that we couldn't in good conscience ignore his plea. Finally, more to get rid of him than anything else, I asked him where the place was.

"Jordan Valley," he said. "Over in the New Territories. It's called Cemetery Number Seven."

"I'll think about it, Mr. Pang," I said. "Maybe later we can do something. We don't have the time or the money to go over there now."

To my relief, he finally left, but not before promising that I hadn't seen the last of him. Sure enough, he was back in a few days, this time with two friends, who grinned and nodded wordlessly as he talked. And he kept returning, sometimes alone, sometimes with others, refusing to take no for an answer, constantly insisting that we go with him to see for ourselves how these refugees lived.

"Mollie," I said one night, "I'm going to have to go with this man or he'll drive me nuts."

"Then go," she said. "Maybe that will get him off your back."

"I can't believe he's on the level."

"I don't think he is either," she said. "But Cemetery Number Seven must really be pretty bad or he wouldn't dare take you there after talking about it so much."

The next time Mr. Pang came around, Amelia, Philip and I went to Jordan Valley with him. I took the others along partly to interpret, for I didn't trust Mr. Pang, and partly to help me check the situation. It turned out to be just as bad as Mr. Pang had said it was.

The abandoned cemetery was on a mountainside full of mean little shacks and hovels made of rotting wood, rusty tin, cardboard, paper, cloth, and anything else that might serve as protection from the weather. It was similar to the squatters' village across the road from our house on Oxford Road, only several times as big and even flimsier. The only solid building was what had once been the cemetery office, a cement structure with three rooms that housed seven families. Even under such real cover, they obviously weren't comfortable. The first thing I noticed when we walked in was a wall covered with thousands of tiny red marks that reached almost to the ceiling. Philip learned they were squashed bedbugs.

While Mr. Pang smirked and rubbed his hands and kept repeating, "See? See? See?" we walked around the valley, picking our way through dirt and garbage past rickety huts which survived only from one typhoon to the next. We stopped here and there, finding someone in almost every shack with a bad cough, skin lesions, or some other evidence of trouble. The only medical care these people had was from mobile clinics which stayed for a day, then went on. These were hardly effective, for they didn't come around often enough or regularly enough to handle cases requiring continual treatment.

When Philip and Amelia agreed there was a definite need for a permanent clinic, we decided to talk it over with the staff and see what arrangements we could make. It would mean more work for everyone until we added to our personnel, which, in turn, meant raising more money. However, despite the obvious drawback of having to take Mr. Pang with the rest of the operation, Jordan Valley seemed a logical place for us to go. We never called it anything else. Cemetery Number Seven was hardly appropriate as a name for a medical unit.

After Hong Kong officials assured us there were no immediate plans for rehabilitating the area and that we were free to do as we pleased there, Dorothy Plant got permission from the Crown Lands and Survey Department to convert the little office building into a clinic. Since this would take some time, we started in the open air because there were so many people in need of immediate attention.

Our first clinic was primitive, noisy, and confusing, with kids yelling and babies crying and people squabbling as they jockeyed for position in line. We could control this situation in the Walled City clinic, which was small and compact, and on the *Yauh Oi*, where we had a good registration system, but all we could do at Jordan Valley was beg everyone to quiet down and wait his turn. The only modern equipment we had was what we could carry in a medical kit. We brought two wooden horses and put planks across them, and that was our "pharmacy," where Philip passed out medicines as I prescribed them. I laid out my examination tools at one end, while the head of the line of patients stood at the other. We looked down throats, took temperatures, checked blood pressures, and listened to heartbeats right out in the open. For privacy, we hung a piece of canvas across a couple of stakes and whenever necessary Amelia and I retired behind it with the patient who, in the absence of an examination table, sat on a camp stool.

This went on for several weeks. One day some Chinese students from the nearby University of Hong Kong stopped by and asked if they could help. A number of them got together and built a concrete pathway up the mountain, hoisting buckets of cement and water on a makeshift tramway until they finished the job. It made life easier in normal times and was a godsend after typhoons, for it gave the people direct access to the mountain when rebuilding their huts. We still use it visiting patients too weak to come to the clinic, and we still have student volunteers from the university.

Whether we liked it or not, the ever-present Mr. Pang, who hovered around like a vulture, was our closest contact with the people. He told them when to expect us, kept the lines in order, and helped out in various other ways. The people seemed to respect him, and there was no doubt he could handle them better than we could. Perhaps, I decided, I had done this man a gross injustice. Perhaps he had truly come to us out of the kindness of his heart and wasn't looking for anything for himself at all.

Then one day he asked me for a little job. He wanted to be caretaker of the clinic for a ridiculously small monthly fee. He pointed out that Jordan Valley was a very tough area and that somebody should be around to keep vandals from breaking in. After I agreed to hire him, he suggested we build him a little house nearby while the workmen fixing up the clinic were still around. When I demurred, he asked how we could expect him to take care of the place if he didn't live there. It was too logical an argument to turn down, so Mr. Pang got his little house to go with his little job.

On the day we officially opened the clinic, with welcoming speeches from local and colony dignitaries, there was a big crowd on the driveway alongside the building watching something that didn't seem to have any connection with the ceremonies. When I reached there I saw it was a medicine show. While a pitchman pointed, his helper stood with his head down, his shoulders sagging, and his tongue hanging out, then the pitchman handed him a big red pill. The helper swallowed it, stood up straight, squared his shoulders, and grinned, while the pitchman sold pills to the audience.

I blew up. As I started for the platform, Mr. Pang tried to hurry around behind me. I grabbed him, demanded an explanation, and told him to get those people out of there and see that they never came back. After a weak protest, he went up and stopped the act.

That was only the beginning. One day when somebody caught Mr. Pang collecting money from a patient in return for a place near the head of the line, I told him he was a caretaker, not an usher, and that I didn't expect to see him around the patients during clinic hours. A month after he moved into the house, we got a whopping electric bill. On investigation we found that he had sneaked a line in off our outlet and started a laundry. He was using the electricity for the ironing.

Not long after that he opened a refreshment stand where the medicine show had been, and drew off our electricity again. That time we put a separate meter on his outlet and made him pay his share of the bill. Then we began missing items from the clinic. We suspected Mr. Pang because he had a key, but we couldn't prove anything. After a while we changed the lock, and that was the end of the pilfering. It was not the end of Mr. Pang, however. Although we fired him, we let him stay in his house and continue to run his refreshment stand because we didn't want to make an enemy of him.

As we expanded, more and more people came to work for us. While our short-term volunteers, mostly from the States, Australia, and New Zealand, gave us a tremendous lift, the backbone of Project Concern was the paid personnel who were with us on a permanent basis. We couldn't give them anywhere nearly what they were worth, but their demands were modest and few left because they weren't getting enough money.

In Hong Kong competent medical help was not hard to find because there were so many trained refugee doctors from Communist China unable to get licenses. Many came to Project Concern willing to accept subsistence wages. I hated to ask them to work for so little, but it was the only way we could function. Money was such a problem we had to cut corners wherever possible. By the time we opened the Jordan Valley clinic, we were getting a million dollars' worth of doctors for the price of hospital orderlies.

We divided our staff into two teams, each consisting of a registered doctor, four who were unlicensed, a nurse, a lab technician, a pharmacist, and two registrars. Each team worked three days on the boat and split the other three days between the Walled City and Jordan Valley. In this way we always kept the *Yauh Oi* covered and did a reasonably adequate job in the other clinics.

Mollie has always said that the only difference between our personal life in the States and in Hong Kong was that we were together more as a family unit in Hong Kong. This was particularly true when we moved aboard the *Yauh Oi* to live in September, 1963, after the Fleeners and Dennis Wong went home. After school the children spent almost all their time on the boat, where they played, studied, and organized parties for other children in the area. When the spirit moved them, they did simple chores in the clinic, such as helping to pack pills, stamping cards, or distributing vitamins.

The boys went to British schools in Kowloon, Scott to Kowloon Junior School, Keith and Pate to King George V School. Jan went to a Cantonese kindergarten where she was the only English-speaking child, and soon her Chinese was the best of any Westerner aboard. A girl named Quon Ying, who was about eleven, absolutely adored Jan, following her around all the time. She waited for Jan to get home from school on weekdays, and on Saturdays picked her up right after breakfast to take her visiting around the shelter. The kids would hop from boat to boat, and sometimes we wouldn't see them from one meal to the next.

Quon Ying, a jolly youngster who was always either grinning or giggling, couldn't speak a word of English. She was so good-natured and got such a kick out of listening to us that we all tested our Cantonese on her. As usual, mine was the worst, and she broke up every time I opened my mouth. Only Jan could actually converse with her. The rest of us could just laugh with her.

We gave Pete a sampan for Christmas and it took him days to learn to scull it. He and Scott went out in it the first day, and when they weren't back by suppertime I went to the roof to look for them. Since they were only about forty yards away, I yelled for them to come in.

"We're trying, Dad," Pete called. "But we can't control it."

After telling Mollie we'd be back in a few minutes, I went over in Ah Tai's taxi to help them. Waving off her offers of assistance, I climbed aboard and got the oar into place, but then went around in circles, just as the boys had. There's a trick to poling a sampan under the best of conditions, and that day a strong tide was running. I finally had to call a grinning Ah Tai to come aboard and pole us home—three-quarters of an hour late for supper.

Mollie prepared American breakfasts and suppers, but we had a Chinese cook to fix lunches. Counting staff, volunteers, and visitors, we often fed thirty or forty people for lunch. Mollie did the marketing, having learned the little tricks of shopping in Hong Kong when we lived on Oxford Road. She could arrange a delicious meal, complete with rice and about six different dishes to choose from, for no more than a dollar Hong Kong a person, about twenty cents United States. This would include chicken, shrimp, lobster, abalone, fish, beef, or whatever other meats might be available in the markets. Later, when some of the volunteers lived aboard the *Yauh Oi*, the cook stayed over to fix dinners. By then Mollie, tied up with the children and more and more office detail, was too busy to prepare anything but breakfast.

One constant problem was the generator, which was forever going out of whack. We used butane gas for the stove and refrigerator, but the generator supplied the electricity for our lighting, water, and some of the laboratory equipment. Whenever something happened to the generator, which was on an especially built sampan beside the boat, someone had to get a gas lantern and go down to fix it. Keith once saved the *Yauh Oi* when the generator broke. Pate hit his head on a lantern, which upset and scattered burning gas over the deck of their room. Keith rushed upstairs, grabbed an extinguisher and, aiming it from the roof to the floor, doused the fire before any real harm was done. There are still spots all over the room from the foam. A week later the generator's steel fan broke with such a clatter that it scared everyone within hearing distance, and somebody had to climb down to the sampan to fix it. We finally hired a maintenance man whose principal job was to keep the generator going.

You never know exactly what you're getting when you hire help in Hong Kong. A maintenance man may be only a maintenance man, but a chauffeur may be an all-round genius. It was a lucky day for us when Mathew Lin applied for work just when we needed a driver and odd-jobman, for which we could pay $400 Hong Kong a month (about $80 United States). In Mathew we got not only a driver and odd-jobman, but a mechanic, linguist, guide, charmer, wheeler-dealer, organizer, bargainer, and executive.

Very tall for a Chinese—he stands nearly six feet—Mathew, who is about thirty-five, can do almost anything. Although his education stopped at the fifth grade, he speaks six languages, including quite adequate English. Wrapped up in Project Concern, he actually puts its needs before his own, doing anything we ask and more that we don't think of. He shows visitors around, both on and off the boat. He fixes what goes wrong. He finds out what we need, then gets it for unbelievably low prices. He runs parties and contests for the kids. He has everyone's respect. Men are drawn to him and women flip over him (futilely,

I might add, since he has a wife and four children to whom he is devoted). It wasn't long before we began promoting him to more responsible jobs. Now Field Director of Project Concern in Hong Kong, he still doesn't confine his activities to any one place. When I'm in Hong Kong, I never know whether I'll find him in shorts astride the balky generator next to the *Yauh Oi* or in a business suit tapping thanks with his fingertips to a *foky* at *yum cha* while beating down a price for something we need.

He came to us when we were dickering with a contractor to fix up the old cemetery office at Jordan Valley. We got an estimate of $13,000 Hong Kong, which seemed reasonable enough for transforming a dirty, bare old building into a clinic with three examining rooms, a lab, a pharmacy, and a waiting room. When we told Mathew about it, he hit the ceiling.

"That's ridiculous," he said. "Let me go out and price the materials and labor. I know I can do better than that." He got the job done for $2,000 Hong Kong.

I asked Mathew one day how much it would cost to build a basketball court for the kids at Jordan Valley. He told me not to worry about it, then rounded up about twenty Jordan Valley people. In two weeks they built a whole playground, with the basketball court in one corner. When the bus motor began to peter out, we got a price of $1,100 Hong Kong from the Volkswagen people to fix it. Mathew had it done by a Chinese mechanic for $600. When somebody gave us money to build a monkey bar for the children at Jordan Valley, Mathew did it himself. He once even got the landlord at our downtown office to cut the rent fifty dollars a month. When I asked him how he did it, Mathew replied, "I just tell him beautiful words."

Mathew had once been in the exporting business with two Americans, acting as the Chinese representative in the colony. When the business collapsed, he lost everything he owned. In Hong Kong, a business failure is no disgrace. When it happens, the usual reaction is to forget debts and start all over. Mathew, feeling his honor was at stake, paid off every cent he owed working at odd jobs. He was still paying when he came to us.

He has stayed in the face of much better offers. Recently he turned down the job of assistant manager of the Fortuna Hotel in Hong Kong with the understanding that he would become manager within a reasonable time. He preferred to remain with Project Concern. Mollie asked him why.

"You could make so much more money in the business world," she said. "What makes you fight for us the way you do and stick with us even when things get rough?"

"Well," he said, "I've had business failures. I've had problems. I've had bad luck. I finally decided I must have been a very bad person in my last life. If I live this life as good as I possibly can, maybe the next time I come back I'll have better luck."

CHAPTER

11

By the summer of 1963 our clinics were functioning well, with an expanding staff of professionals and volunteers always on hand to keep things going. Although money was a problem—I suppose it always will be—we were generally in pretty good shape. We could handle about twelve hundred patients a week in our two boat clinics and in the Walled City and Jordan Valley. We enjoyed cordial relations with everyone around us. Some of the colony's hospitals took our patients, other relief agencies recognized us as equals, and the official, business, and social community accepted us as part of the local scene.

It was time for me to think of moving on. The world is full of people in desperate need of medical care, and only a small fraction of them are in Hong Kong. If Project Concern were to do the job it was conceived to do, it could not confine its activities to one place. As long as I was needed in Hong Kong, that was where I belonged. As soon as we reached the point where others could do as well, I belonged somewhere else. It had happened in Tijuana; now it was happening in Hong Kong.

Furthermore, Hong Kong provided too many distractions. This huge, glamorous, beautiful city is a major stopover for tourists from all over the world. Many found their way out to the *Yauh Oi*, where they were always welcome. We were glad to show visitors around, for there was no better way of letting people know what we were trying to do. On the other hand, we were almost killed by kindness. We could have been someone's dinner guests every night in the week. It was impossible to accept all the invitations, yet we hated to turn anyone down. While extremely flattering, the situation was a bit embarrassing. More important, it cut deeply into the time needed for my work. On top of that, as long as I remained available in Hong Kong I was expected to represent Project Concern at all manner of social and business functions. I got out of as many as I could, but some were impossible to refuse. Luncheons, meetings, banquets, official gatherings, and conferences often took me away from the clinic and sometimes kept me away all day.

Mollie, who had been through far worse with me, accepted my desire to move with heroic calm. When I first mentioned it to her, she said, "I knew things were going too smoothly to last." But she smiled when she said it, and quickly added, "But it's true that you don't have to be here yourself any more to keep the clinics going."

We already had a qualified doctor to replace me. Dr. John Wong, from New Westminster, British Columbia,

Canada, had agreed to come to Hong Kong with his wife. He could supervise all the clinics, and as a competent secretary, she would be helpful in that capacity. After their arrival, I could leave any time without weakening our operation.

I started keeping my eyes open for a likely place to start a new Project Concern clinic. One day in the Sunday supplement of the Hong Kong *Tiger Standard* I read that there were no doctors in Bhutan, easternmost of the three tiny Himalayan kingdoms between India and Tibet. (The other two are Nepal and Sikkim.) I called on a Mr. Pandit, the writer of the piece, who promised to arrange for me to meet members of the ruling family, who came to Hong Kong periodically. Not long after that he introduced me to Tashi Dorji, sister of Jig-me Dorji, prime minister of Bhutan. Tremendously enthusiastic about our going in there, she invited me to Thimbu, the capital, in April, 1964, to meet her brother and the king, Maharajah Jig-me Dorji Wan-chuk. This suited us very well. Mollie had close friends in Bangkok whom she had wanted to visit ever since we had gone to the Orient. She could stay with them while I went on to Bhutan, and I could pick her up on the way back to Hong Kong.

From time to time in the next few months I had meetings with various Indian civilians and officials, including Mr. Branchabee, the First Secretary of the Indian Consulate in Hong Kong. Everyone assured me there was plenty of work to be done all over India and smaller nations like Bhutan which are dependent on her in some way or another. Through Mr. Branchabee I made arrangements to visit several communities and confer with Indian medical officials who would help us set up a Project Concern program anywhere in that part of the world. At one point Mr. Branchabee even urged me to consider a pilot program in his home village about two hundred miles from Bombay.

On January 22, 1964, during a busy session on the *Yauh*

Oi, a lanky, handsome man of about fifty, typically British in appearance, came aboard to see me.

"I am Dr. Basil Aldwell," he said. "I've heard about Project Concern, and I understand you are planning to expand."

"We're thinking of going to Bhutan," I said.

"Would you consider South Vietnam?" he asked.

"All I know about South Vietnam is what I read in the newspapers," I said. "In view of the war, I would presume we'd have trouble getting in there."

"I've just come from there, Dr. Turpin. I spent two years among the Montagnard Kohos as part of a New Zealand medical team, sent there under a government program which just ended. The Montagnards are mountain people in the central highlands, near the Cambodian border. There are about sixty thousand, who must be among the poorest, sickest, most neglected men, women, and children in the world."

The more Dr. Aldwell talked, the deeper my interest. At noon I took him over to the American consulate to see Herman Washington, who agreed that an American relief agency working among the Montagnards was an excellent idea, not only for humanitarian purposes but as a gesture of good will. By the time we were back on the boat, I was ready to go to South Vietnam immediately with Basil Aldwell to see for myself the conditions he described.

Again Mollie took my ideas in stride. She knew I was a creature of impulse, but she also knew that my instincts seldom led me astray. She knew, too, that my taking a quick, exploratory trip to South Vietnam didn't necessarily mean I intended to open a clinic there. I would not change my plans to go to India and Bhutan in April, because I wanted to see what the need was there. On my return from India we could then decide which move to make, although I was already more inclined toward South Vietnam. In any event, we would only postpone but not cancel India or its environs as a future site for a Project Concern clinic.

On January 26, four days after Basil came aboard the *Yauh Oi* for the first time, he and I flew to Saigon. After a night at the Continental Palace we began a round of calls on doctors and officials, some of whom were discouraging (one said it was "too dangerous," another advised returning immediately to Hong Kong), but most were helpful and cooperative. We had lunch with Dr. Jenny Singleton of the Tom Dooley Foundation, who took us to meet Madame Ngai, a woman who cared for five hundred orphan children. A person of such great warmth that I didn't have to understand her speech to understand her, she reminded me of Mrs. Maria Mesa of Casa de Todos. She was just as dedicated to her Vietnamese youngsters as Mrs. Mesa was to her little Mexicans. Before the day was over I met more members of the Dooley Foundation, including Dr. Manny Vourgaropoulos, who had been one of Dr. Dooley's closest associates. I also had a warm meeting with Bill Prowell, administrative chief of Care Medico in Saigon, who later became one of my closest friends and strongest backers. Among other things, Bill, a Southerner about my age, gave us the use of his office facilities whenever we were in Saigon.

On the day after our arrival in Vietnam, Basil and I flew on a commercial DC-3 to DaLat, the capital of Tuyen Duc province. The trip was over lush green jungle, snaking rivers, and spacious plantations, country which looked strangely like Kentucky and Tennessee. At DaLat, a lovely resort city in the mountains which served as a rest and recreation area for combat troops and Vietnamese officials, we were met by Basil's good friend, Dr. Jean Louis, director of the Institut Pasteur. The Institute was producing vast amounts of cholera vaccine to fight an epidemic then prevalent. Dr. Louis and his wife took us there first, then to

111

lunch, and later on a drive out into the countryside to visit some of the nearby villages.

I was shocked at what I saw. The villages were unfamiliar, but, except for the special characteristics of their race, the people looked like starving people everywhere. There were children with stomachs distended from hunger. There were bare-bosomed, painfully thin mothers trying to nurse babies with nothing to give them. There were the same telltale evidences of the diseases of the poor which characterized Tijuana, the Walled City, Jordan Valley, and Yaumati—acute malnutrition, skin lesions, the choking cough of respiratory disorders.

Here was a need far beyond any I had ever before seen, a need for kindness and sympathy and friendship and love as well as for medical treatment. Right in the midst of a war-torn nation on which were focused the eyes of the whole world, a forgotten people were living in the Dark Ages, sick, starving, neglected. Few cared about them, and only a handful had time to do anything for them. They were born and lived and died in the same primitive atmosphere their ancestors had. Long before we returned to DaLat that day I knew Tuyen Duc province would have to be the base of Project Concern's next clinic.

I met Colonel De, the provincial governor, a short, slender Vietnamese with dedication, energy, and vitality. So eager to win the confidence of the Montagnards that he learned to speak their language and to sing their mountain songs, he had a Koho Montagnard assistant. He welcomed me with open arms, promised to do anything he could to help me, and told me about DaMpao, the abandoned Special Forces ("Green Beret") camp on top of the hill overlooking the Dung River.

At the bachelor officer's quarters, where I stayed in DaLat, I met Major "Digger" Moravek—Digger was the only name by which I ever knew him—one of the most comforting, confidence-inspiring men I have ever known. Not much over thirty-five, he was a college professor from Oklahoma who looked the part with his bushy brown mustache, his horn-rimmed glasses, and his pipe, which rarely left his mouth. A tough, nerveless fighting man whom the Viet Cong, I was told, actually went out of their way to avoid, Digger knew the Montagnards as well as any American. As security chief of the province, he was Colonel De's American counterpart and the Colonel's almost constant companion. Possessed of an uncanny knack of being where he was most needed, Digger was a careful optimist who, while giving assurance that everything would be all right, was always prepared for the worst, often anticipating trouble before it happened. He moved with the speed and grace of a cat when he had to, but seemed lankily lazy when things were quiet.

He thought it was a great idea to convert the building on the hill at DaMpao into a hospital. His promise to help was more than an empty gesture, for if we went in there, our security would be his responsibility. Although we would be protected by Vietnamese and Koho troops supplied by Colonel De, we would be under Digger's wing and, in case of an emergency requiring a take over by the American military, his orders. However, he didn't anticipate any such trouble for us. He told me that if he didn't think it was safe enough for women as well as men he would never let us go in there. What pleased him most was the same thing that had pleased Herman Washington—the good will we would build for the United States among the people of the central highlands.

"They know us only as soldiers," he said. "It's time someone came to help them, not just fight for them. They have no idea what the fighting is about anyhow."

The first Koho I met was K'Moung, who lived in the village of DaMpao, at the foot of the hill where the hospital would be. Trained by the Special Forces, K'Moung was at home among Americans. He spoke some English and had even learned a little about first aid. I talked with him two or three times, for I pictured him as a key man in a plan to train the people themselves in the rudiments of first aid and simple medical examination and care. Eventually, K'Moung became my interpreter and most devoted Koho assistant.

Since he had no title or even a first name as far as I knew, I called him "Mr. K'Moung," which seemed to please him no end. This set a precedent we later followed with all our male medical aides. Even as students we called them "Mister."

For two weeks I shuttled back and forth between Saigon and DaLat, with frequent side trips to DaMpao and other villages in Tuyen Duc province. I was amazed at the primitive life the Koho people led. Some hadn't seen a village until a few years before. Clad only in loincloths, they had been living like animals in the jungle, in trees and caves and the rudest of shelters. When one got sick they all got sick, and when they recovered, it was a miracle. Too many didn't. The death rate was appalling, the life span less than forty years.

One of my last visits before returning to Hong Kong was at the Ministry of Health in Saigon. Dr. Vuong Quang Truong, the Minister, seemed a bit hesitant about Project Concern, pointing out that Dr. Aldwell's New Zealand team hadn't lasted, and asking what guarantee I could give him that we would.

"We are not a government agency," I reminded him. "We are a private American medical-relief agency, raising money on our own. We built several medical teams in Hong Kong and we can do the same here." Only then did he give me a go-ahead.

At a party that Bill Prowell gave for me that night, Jeff Farrell, his assistant at Care Medico, told me he had some leave coming and asked if I minded his accompanying me to Hong Kong. Jeff was in the national spotlight in 1960 when he successfully qualified for the United States Olympic swimming team only six days after an appendectomy. I not only was glad to have him with me on the airplane, but invited him to stay with us on the *Yauh Oi*. A skinny, boyish-looking six-footer of twenty-eight, he had helped me in many ways in South Vietnam. He attracted friends wherever he went, for he had a bubbling enthusiasm that drew people to him, and I liked him tremendously, as I knew Mollie would. On the plane to Hong Kong we sat opposite Ambassador and Mrs. Henry Cabot Lodge and their very charming twenty-one-year-old niece, Emily Alexander. While Jeff was trying to figure out a way to meet her, he noticed Mrs. Lodge fumbling for a match. Although he didn't smoke himself, Jeff always carried matches, probably for just such emergencies, and offered Mrs. Lodge a light. Soon we were all involved in an animated conversation. By the time we reached Hong Kong, Jeff and Emily were such good friends that she agreed to let him show her around the colony.

Although I invited the Ambassador and his wife to visit the *Yauh Oi*, I never expected them to accept, since they are very busy people with many social and business obligations. But one morning at breakfast Jeff asked, "Jim, did you mean that invitation to the Lodges to see the boat?"

"I sure did," I said. "I wish they'd come, but I suppose they'll never find the time."

"Mrs. Lodge asked me last night if eleven this morning would be convenient for you."

"Are you kidding?"

"No, I'm perfectly serious," Jeff said. "They really want to come."

"Hey, Mollie," I yelled, "get out the red carpet! This is a big day for Project Concern."

It was, too. The Ambassador and his wife, escorted by Emily and Jeff, came aboard on the dot of eleven and stayed about an hour. We took them all over the *Yauh Oi* and the *Ming Ling*, and they seemed sincerely interested and impressed with everything. When it was time for them to leave, Mrs. Lodge asked, "When are you coming to Saigon?"

"In about a month," said Mollie.

"Don't think of going to a hotel when you get there," Mrs. Lodge said. "Just come and stay with us. We have plenty of room, and we would love to have you."

Two days later we saw Jeff off on his return to Saigon. The last thing he said before boarding the plane was, "I'll see you there. And when you're ready, maybe we can work together."

In the meantime, I was busy preparing for the trip to India. This was originally planned primarily as a tour of Bhutan, but Mr. Branchabee told me of so many other places that needed help that I decided to see some of them. It was this trip that Mollie would take as far as Bangkok, stopping with me in South Vietnam first. Besides Saigon, she also wanted to go to DaMpao. I was a little dubious, but she insisted that if it was safe enough for nurses it was safe enough for her and if not, it wasn't safe enough for me. In the face of such logic, I agreed to take her there.

The Bhutan project died when I received a letter from Miss Dorji to the effect that her country could not accept our offer of assistance. She gave no reason, but I later learned that the United States had rejected a Bhutanese request for several million dollars because India might disapprove, causing some anti-American feeling in Bhutan. This eliminated the original reason for my going to India at all, but I couldn't change my plans because of important appointments Mr. Branchabee had made for me. Besides, I wanted to see the country for its future Project Concern possibilities.

I already had a doctor lined up to help me get started in DaMpao. Through the Australian Jaycees I had been in touch with Dr. Godfrey Gapp, who lived with his wife and two children in the tiny Queensland community of Clifton. Although in his forties, Goff Gapp had been a doctor only a short time. When he heard we were planning to open a hospital in South Vietnam he asked to join us for a few months, agreeing to come first to Hong Kong to get acquainted with Project Concern and our procedures.

He arrived just before Mollie and I left. Blond, blue-eyed, plump, of medium height, Goff was so shy he seemed unimpressive at first, but in the clinic he was a different man. The sight of people in pain brought out a glow of compassion that reminded me of Maria Mesa. Goff couldn't bear to see anyone suffer. He wanted to cure every ill, to ease every pang, to make the crippled walk, to bring the dying back to life. His deep sympathy for humanity came into sharpest focus when he saw the Walled City and Jordan Valley for the first time, for he had never been exposed to such abject suffering or such obvious need for medical care before. The trip left him actually shaking. I was with him only a few days before Mollie and I took off for South Vietnam, but that was enough to convince me we couldn't have found a more perfect man for the job.

While I was showing Mollie the abandoned Special Forces camp at DaMpao a few days later some French Catholic priests drove up the hill with a sick Koho woman on a stretcher and asked if the hospital were open yet. It wasn't, of course, but I said I'd be glad to look at her. She appeared to have cancer of the pelvis. All I could do was give her something from my medical kit to ease the pain and advise them to take her to the government hospital in DaLat. Before Mollie and I left, a blind man suffering from acute glaucoma was led up by relatives. After examining him, I was almost physically sick with regret, for I knew I could have helped him if I had seen him sooner.

"These people here have nothing," I told Mollie. "They need us so badly that we've just got to come in as soon as we can."

Back in Saigon we were met at the airport by Jeff Farrell, who bundled us into his Care Medico station wagon for the ride to town. Instead of the Hotel Continental Palace, where we had reservations, he took us to an estate on the city's outskirts.

"Where are we?" Mollie asked.

"This is the Lodges' home," Jeff said. "When they heard you were coming, they insisted you stay here. They're not in at the moment, but they expect you later for cocktails. In the meantime, make yourselves comfortable."

Then, after letting us into a little guest cottage, he told us he'd see us for dinner and drove off before either of us had time to express surprise or thanks.

Although the Ambassador, then a possible Republican presidential candidate, was terribly busy, he relaxed with us at cocktails and both he and his wife asked all sorts of questions about our plans. The thing that impressed me most was Mrs. Lodge's repeated expressions of envy of our opportunity to make real friends of the people of South Vietnam. This is a problem for Americans, especially those in the highest echelons. Both Lodges stressed the importance of the type of work we planned to do, and both heartily approved our going into the central highlands. They never lost interest in Project Concern. The Ambassador now serves on our International Advisory Committee.

We flew to Bangkok, where Mollie stayed with Jane and John Cobb, old friends of ours from Atlanta, while I went on to India. There, I learned that the Jaycees knew about Project Concern and hoped we would open clinics in this vast, poverty-stricken country. In New Delhi I met General Lahksmanon, the head of the Red Cross, who said, "Dr. Turpin, you could blindfold yourself before a map of India, throw a dart, and settle wherever it landed. I'll guarantee you'd be needed and welcome there."

He was particularly happy to know that we had no religious or political affiliations. At his suggestion, I decided to go to Orissa, a seacoast state of about fourteen million people with practically no medical care. I flew to Bhubaneswhar, the capital, where Dr. Rao, the superintendent, took me through his modest hospital, the only one in the entire state. He later drove me to the hill country, fifteen miles away, where thousands of people live and die without ever seeing a doctor.

"One hundred and fifty hospital beds for fourteen million people aren't very many, Dr. Turpin," Dr. Rao said. "Whenever you are ready for Orissa, Orissa will be ready for you."

Someday I hope Project Concern will be ready for that area around Bhubaneswhar. It was worth the trip just to learn about the place and its terrible need for help. I arrived back in Hong Kong on May 25. I had planned to go to DaMpao with Goff the first week in June to open the hospital, but there was too much to do in Hong Kong. When Goff volunteered to go alone, I decided to let him. I could meet him there in a couple of weeks.

I knew of no better man to introduce Project Concern to the Kohos and Vietnamese of the mountain country, for this shy, small-town Australian doctor was a genius at making friends, particularly among the little people. In the short time he was in Hong Kong, where he lived aboard the *Yauh Oi*, he became close to more of them than the rest of us put together. He spent hours with our own Chinese volunteers, nurses, attendants and unregistered doctors from the mainland, and more hours with our neighbors in the typhoon shelter. He went to back-alley restaurants and out-of-the-way water-front spots, boarded junks and sampans, and visited homes in Jordan Valley and the Walled City.

He had promised his wife to be home after three months, and had already been in Hong Kong for two. Now he was more anxious even than I to go to South Vietnam because he wanted to work there before returning to Australia. I spent hours briefing him, telling him of the things he should do and the people he should meet, especially the American and Vietnamese officials in Saigon and Digger Moravek, Colonel De and K'Moung in DaLat and DaMpao. I had no qualms about Goff getting along with K'Moung, for Goff could get along with anyone. He was familiar with the plans to train Kohos in medical procedures, and said he would have the program under way before he left there.

We saw him off on June 2. Although I didn't reach DaMpao myself for nearly three weeks, I like to think of Goff's departure as the date we started Project Concern in South Vietnam. By the time I arrived, he had done the spadework on the hospital and among the Kohos. All I had to do was pick it up from there.

CHAPTER

12

In South Vietnam it's always hotly sticky in a DC-3, and it was particularly so on that mid-June morning when Guy Brehon and I flew from Saigon to DaLat. The old airplane, built more for durability than speed or comfort, was like a furnace. Noisy little fans, hardly creating a breeze, fought a losing battle with the humidity, while everyone aboard spent the whole trip mopping brows and necks with sweat-soaked handkerchiefs. Guy and I were both too keyed up to mind. Project Concern in South Vietnam was open for business in DaMpao. Heat or no heat, all we wanted to do was get there, I to relieve Goff, Guy to assume the duties of camp manager. Guy, who was French by birth and Australian by adoption, had asked to join us when I met him in Orange, New South Wales, on my last trip there. I was delighted to have him.

As we neared DaLat we could see the round, tightly-fenced, well-trenched "new life" hamlets of the Montagnard tribesmen, villages especially built to rescue them from the Viet Cong and the jungle where they had been living in another century. Each tiny community was an entity of its own, independent of the others yet part of the over-all plan to introduce these primitive people to civilization. From the air, the villages looked like forts which, in a sense, they were. Scattered here and there were rice paddies, flat, mucky, and, with Viet Cong in and out of the area, often traps for whites and Vietnamese alike. Periodic puffs of smoke and flashes of fire gave evidence that real danger lurked there.

We saw paved roads leading out of DaLat and narrowing into crude dirt lanes through the jungles and the paddies and in and out of the villages. As we gradually settled in toward the small air strip, the lanes disappeared and only the pavements were visible, looking like highways to nowhere. I knew better. One of those dusty lanes led to DaMpao. It would not be long before Guy and I would be traveling on it, a trip more nerve-racking than actually dangerous. The Viet Congs stayed off the roads in the daytime, or at least most of them did. And, since Colonel De had assured us of good security at DaMpao, there was little to worry about once we got there.

It was still early when we landed, for we had left Saigon at seven-thirty in the morning. Goff had organized a ceremony to introduce the Village Medical Officer program, scheduling it for our arrival at DaMpao at nine-thirty. It's an hour by air to DaLat from Saigon and another hour by car to DaMpao from DaLat.

The wheels of the DC-3 touched the paved landing strip with a bump and we taxied to the small administration building after a last loud roar of the motors. As Guy and I stood in the aisle with the other steaming passengers waiting for the door to open, the only sound in the cabin was the tired whirr of the fans, still trying feebly to fight the stifling heat. Only when the doors finally swung open to let in the first fresh air we had breathed since leaving Saigon did we begin to feel comfortable.

To the best of my knowledge, Tuyen Duc province enjoys the mildest weather in South Vietnam. The mornings are bright and clear and dry and the afternoons and evenings humid or wet depending upon the season, while the thermometer usually remains in a temperature range between sixty and eighty-five. Now it was nearer eighty-five, warm on the ground but delightfully cool after an hour in a broiling airplane.

Digger, complete with mustache, horn-rimmed glasses, pipe, and highly polished field boots, was standing at the foot of the steps when we came down.

"Hello, Jim," he said. "You look fine."

"Nice to see you, Digger. Thanks for meeting us."

"No trouble."

I introduced him to Guy, then we picked up our luggage and followed him to his jeep. After we climbed aboard and headed along the paved road north of the airport, Digger said, "Colonel De sends his greetings. He'll meet us at the ceremony in DaMpao."

"How's everything there?"

"Wonderful, thanks to Goff."

"He's a dandy," I said.

"The people love him."

"Everybody does. I wish he didn't have to leave, but he promised his family not to stay more than three months."

We had started on the main highway between DaLat and Saigon, where the going was smooth, but now we turned right into a narrow, pitted, half-paved, one-lane road and passed a Vietnamese village. These are larger, older, and more sinister than the Koho "new life" hamlets, for you never know whether the people are loyal or not. Viet Cong can move in and out of Vietnamese villages without being detected because they are Vietnamese. Since Kohos—Montagnards—look altogether different, their "new life" village populations can be much more easily controlled. There is ill feeling between Kohos and Vietnamese, as senseless as the ill feeling between whites and Negroes in the deep South and as hard to break down.

"How's security, Digger?" I said, as we jounced along.

He took his pipe from his mouth, stared at a Koho village as we passed it, then said, "It's all right, Jim. We haven't had any serious trouble around DaMpao for a year now. That should make it easier for you."

We reached the end of what little pavement had been left and he shifted the jeep into four-wheel drive to cope with the huge, muddy ruts that would test the strength of the threaded, deeply-grooved tires. From here on we would be passing rice paddies and jungles as well as villages. There was a shot off in the distance, but Digger paid no attention. Shots off in the distance are part of the atmosphere of rural South Vietnam.

Digger honked at a group of small boys tending a herd of water buffalo up ahead, and they scattered, leading their clumsy animals off the muddy road into the thick green foliage on both sides until we passed. Some Koho Self-Defense Corps soldiers in loincloths waved their carbines and smiled when they recognized the markings on our jeep. They looked perfectly natural on that road, yet where else in the world could you see a combination of loincloths and carbines? Loincloths and battering rams, or loincloths and bows and arrows, or perhaps even loincloths and blunderbusses, but carbines? When I commented on it, Digger said, "That's the kind of war this is."

We passed a company of Vietnamese soldiers, who stood by the side of the road as we bumped along by them. They, too, smiled and waved their carbines, and some, recognizing Digger, called him by his rank of major.

"How do you tell which ones are Viet Cong, Digger?"
I said. "They all look alike."

"The Viet Cong don't smile. They shoot."

"In the daytime?"

"They're not out on the roads in the daytime," Digger
said.

When we rounded a final bend we could look up to the
rocky rise that was DaMpao. The hospital site jutted up
beyond the far side of a flat valley where there were several
Koho villages. The old Special Forces camp commanded
a view across the valley to the east, was bordered on the
west by the Dung River, and on the north by still higher
mountains. The village of DaMpao was on the south, the
direction from which we were approaching. We passed it,
and as we began to climb could hear the murmur of many
voices.

"It was deserted when I saw it last," I said.

"It's not deserted now, Jim," Digger said. "Goff's students are up there, and their relatives, and their friends,
and even the chiefs of their villages. And they're all waiting for you."

"How many?"

"Goff expects thirty or more. Judging by the voices I'd
say there were at least that many."

Amazed, I said, "They don't even know me."

"They know who you are. This is a big deal for them.
They've never had a doctor before."

We entered the heavy gate past a Vietnamese guard who
waved and grinned at us, then pulled up to the front of
the hospital building. Several Vietnamese dignitaries, military and civilian, stood on the right near a portly white-
coated figure I recognized at once as Goff. He was striding
over as Digger put on the brakes. I hopped out to shake
hands, then went to greet Colonel De. After that Goff
introduced us to the other officials, some of whom I already
knew.

"Now I want you to meet our students, Jim," Goff said, motioning me to a group of young people by the door. As they stood, shy and ill at ease, he called, "This is Bac-Si Turpin." Then, to me, "You know K'Moung, of course."

K'Moung, who had already stepped forward, grinned and bowed, and we shook hands.

"This is H'Klas," Goff went on. "D'Gle, K'Chai, K'Chih, K'Sre, K'Bran . . ."

He went through the list of students, who stepped forward as he called their names. D'Gle, K'Moung's wife, and K'Sre were the only women. When I had met the whole class, Goff introduced me to the chiefs, whom he addressed by the names of their villages—DaMpao, Psourr, Riento, DaBrach, Portang, DaMe, Kamboutte, among others. Then he escorted me to the other villagers present, most of whom were in loincloths. One, resplendent in American G.I. scivvies and a T shirt, showed off his costume so proudly I expected him to pirouette so I could see the back as well as the front. The chiefs were dressed slightly better than the others, meaning they wore shirts.

When all the introductions were completed, Goff told the people in his rich Queensland accent that the hospital was now open and anyone anywhere in the area was welcome to use it. He spoke slowly, pausing frequently for K'Moung to interpret along the way. When he had finished, he introduced Colonel De. The provincial chief, well aware that Project Concern would primarily benefit the Montagnard people, did not let the opportunity pass to stress his government's support and cooperation. Speaking in Koho, he carefully explained that we were an international team of doctors, nurses, and technicians who had come to DaMpao to treat and to teach. The chiefs, to whom he addressed his remarks, were obviously satisfied, because they smiled warmly at Goff and me when the Colonel finished. I ended the ceremony with a short talk interpreted by K'Moung.

As the chiefs and other dignitaries began making their way back along the muddy road, dark, ominous clouds rolled across the mountains to the north and rain started streaming down in solid sheets. A chief paused, then turned and, with great dignity, walked slowly back through the downpour. K'Chai, one of the students, went out to meet him. When the chief raised his hand, the youth stopped, then moved over beside me. Realizing the chief had something to say to me, I waited in the rain, where I was joined by K'Moung, who had stepped up to translate.

"Bac-Si," said the chief, "my people are very sick. In my village there is no medicine that works." Putting one hand on K'Chai's shoulder, he added, "Send our young man back to make us strong. We need that above all else." Then, erect and proud, he disappeared in a pelting shower of raindrops the size of marbles.

Eager to see how much had been done and how much remained to be done in the clinic and hospital, I stepped inside. Instead of Goff and the students alone, I found a roomful of patients looking expectantly at me just as patients look at doctors all over the world. I hid my surprise with a genuinely happy grin, waved as I walked across the room, and went on to meet Goff in the examining room.

"I see we have patients already," I said.

"A few have been coming every day," Goff said. "Everyone knew when you would arrive. And the last couple of days Radio DaLat has been broadcasting in Koho and Vietnamese that regular clinic sessions would begin this morning."

There was a slight commotion behind us as two of the students brought an emaciated young Montagnard wife on an improvised stretcher of cut poles and a filthy, worn blanket. Behind them came the woman's husband, followed by the ever-present K'Moung who, I now realized, knew exactly when to be where he was most needed. It took no intensive examination to see that this woman was desperately sick. Her skin, scaly and dirt-caked, hung loosely about slender, delicate bones, while her hands and feet were puffy with the pale edema that indicated starvation.

"Help me, Goff," I said. "She's almost dead."

We pulled at a soiled light-blue-blouse under a hand-woven black cloth about her upper torso, then I caught my breath.

"There's a baby here," I said.

A frail infant was trying vainly to suck from a pendulous dry breast. K'Moung stepped close to me and said, "The father says the child is seven months old, Bac-Si."

"I would have guessed seven weeks."

Goff, who had a stethoscope at the mother's chest, said, "I think she has pulmonary tuberculosis. Her lungs are full of cavitous breath sounds."

"The father says she spits blood," K'Moung said.

"We can get a better look in the minor surgery room," Goff said.

It was the first I knew our minor surgery room was ready. K'Moung, H'Klas, the woman's husband, and I lifted her gently while Goff opened the door and led the way. As we moved slowly, the patient coughed bloody sputum into a soiled cloth in her puffy hand. Her body and clothing reeked of smoke, which I later learned was from open fires in the tiny thatched hovel she shared with her husband and child.

We laid her on a table and Goff, continuing his examination, confirmed his diagnosis of pulmonary tuberculosis. The woman was also suffering from wet beriberi, pellagra, and starvation.

Goff suddenly looked up and said, "Jim, she's pregnant."

"Do we have I.V.?" I said.

"In the storeroom."

"Any beds?"

He nodded.

"Sheets—blankets—vitamins?"

"Enough to get started. You'll need more."

While mother and child were being settled in the hospital, I thought, "There's two lives we owe to Goff. If he hadn't had everything ready we would have lost them both." And as we went back to the clinic, I wished—almost, but not quite aloud—that he didn't have to go home to Australia, for he and Project Concern were made for each other.

Back in the clinic, K'Moung escorted a Koho mother into the examining room. In her arms was a pale, thin three-year-old boy in a deep coma. "She says he has twenty–thirty water bowel movements each day, Bac-Si," K'Moung said. I pinched the boy's dry skin between my fingers. When I let go it stood alone, wrinkled and mounded. His body was yielding all possible fluid from the skin to the circulation.

The child, suffering from bacillary dysentery, would need I.V. feedings and intensive hospital care. When K'Moung told the mother, she went to the waiting room and beckoned, then her husband and three other children followed us to the hospital.

"Tell them to come back tomorrow," I said.

K'Moung shook his head. "They will stay."

I shrugged. Vietnam was no different from Hong Kong. If the patient stayed, the family stayed. If the family left, the patient would leave.

I started the first I.V. feeding, gave the boy, whose name was K'Chong, an initial dose of chloramphenicol, and told H'Klas and K'Chai to measure the amount of each bowel movement. As we prepared to isolate the little patient as much as possible under the circumstances, I stopped long enough to mix some potassium permanganate solution and showed H'Klas and K'Chai how to wash their hands in it.

We saw thirty-five patients that day, including another with bacillary dysentery, one with malaria, and a woman with an ailment I hadn't seen since Coronado—acute anxiety reactions. I hardly believed it at first, but she had all the symptoms. She lay motionless, her breathing regular, her blood pressure, pulse, heart, lungs, abdomen, and eyes normal, and with no unusual odors. When she failed to respond to a pin prick, I recognized her trouble.

Through K'Moung, I asked her husband if she has been upset about anything.

"The war," he said. "It frightens her."

I couldn't do anything about the war, but I could tell him she needed plenty of rest. When she left, I realized that acute anxiety reactions are not limited to the rich of California. The poor of the Montagnard hills of South Vietnam are also susceptible to them.

Only when the last patient had left was I aware that I had not had time to do more than wash up, zip myself into a white jump suit, and have a banana for lunch during a busy, eminently satisfying day. Darkness came with another monsoonal downpour, this one in the late afternoon. From then on we found our way around by candlelight.

Guy, clad in a white shirt, shorts, and knee stockings, was temporarily acting as chef. "Dinner's ready, Jim," he said.

"What are we having?"

"Bananas and powdered milk."

"Don't we have anything but bananas?"

"I got a tip today on some duck eggs. A man promised to bring them up before breakfast."

"What will we have for breakfast if he doesn't?"

"Bananas," Guy said. When I groaned, he added, "Don't worry. I found out where to get a Vietnamese chef in DaLat. I'll pick him up when I go over there to market tomorrow."

"I should have left you there to market today," I said.

That night, Goff's last in DaMpao, we sat around and

talked by the light of our few flickering candles. A generator ordered months before was due any day, but until it came we had to do without electricity. Before going to bed I dictated a tape to Mollie on a portable transistor recorder I had brought along for the purpose. I missed her and the children, but it wouldn't be for long. In another few weeks they would join me for the summer, since Digger and Colonel De has assured me that, for the time being at least, it was perfectly safe.

The last thing I did was look in at the hospital. Our patients, K'Le and her starving child, and the two bacillary dysentery cases, were resting comfortably. So were their relatives.

CHAPTER

13

After breakfast—we had to settle for bananas and powdered milk because Guy couldn't get the duck eggs during the night—I took some dehydrated soup into the hospital for K'Chong, the little boy with dysentery. I was pleased to find him out of his coma, although that was the only improvement in his generally poor condition. Knowing the salt, fluid, and calories in the soup would help him if anything could, I spooned it into his mouth myself. He accepted it eagerly enough, but his face was grave and his eyes fixed on my left ear as he ate. After he finished, I reached for my pen light and shone it first into one eye, then the other. There was no reaction. K'Chong was blind. His father told K'Moung that he always had been.

I was much happier about K'Le's condition. Despite her various ailments and her pregnancy, she showed real improvement. Her breathing was easier, she coughed less, and her chest sounded better. And, thanks to Goff and D'Gle, she had peace of mind about her child. Goff had shown D'Gle how to fix formula, and D'Gle had already fed the youngster, who had slept with his father on a cot beside his mother's bed. Now, as he napped peacefully, there was a touch of color on his face, giving him more the appearance of a growing baby than an emaciated newborn infant.

Before I moved on to look at our other patients, the father spoke to K'Moung and handed him something. "He says his wife will get well now," K'Moung said. "He wants you to have these." K'Moung gave me two small eggs. It was our first payment in DaMpao for professional services rendered.

"Tell him it will take a long time, K'Moung," I said. "Tell him his wife will have to take much medicine, eat plenty of good food here, and let us feed her baby for several weeks before she can go home."

I waited for K'Moung to relay the message, then spoke the first Koho word in my vocabulary, "Ngnai." It means "Thank you," and I wasn't thanking him just for the eggs. I was thanking him for bringing his family to us, for trusting us, for letting us be involved in the lives of his loved ones. I think he understood.

Getting people to trust us, to bring their loved ones to us, to let us become involved in their lives was our hardest job in DaMpao, just as it had been when we first opened the Walled City clinic in Hong Kong. There, we were fortunate in not losing any patients in the first few weeks. In DaMpao we lost two in the first few days. One, a man in the last stages of tuberculosis, died four hours after his arrival. The other was K'Chong, who lived only three days after he was brought in. I had never had much hope for him, but that didn't make his death any easier to take. Death is always painful, that of a child especially so. The only solace in K'Chong's case was that his family, apparently realizing we had done all we could for him, seemed grateful. His parents thanked us before taking his body back to their village for the funeral ceremony.

Twice in our first week we were faced with unusual situations. The first required a makeshift solution that had worked before. A small boy, his skin giving off heat, his nostrils flaring hard, labored breathing, came in obviously suffering from bilateral pneumonia. With no modern facilities, we made a Rube Goldberg steam tent of blankets and plastic tubes, like the one that had saved the lives of the two sick children at Casa de Todos. While waiting until it was ready we administered massive doses of penicillin and added a mist of steam to relax the breathing passages. Then, as a couple of the V.M.O. students kept sponging the fevered body, we sweated out the next few hours. When the temperature broke and the child began breathing easier, I knew we were all right.

The second unusual situation was new to me, at least in my medical career. A delirious woman brought in by some frightened villagers had been bitten an hour before by a green pig snake. The bite was in a bad place, high on one leg, causing enormous swelling which got worse by the minute. K'Moung produced antivenom (which I didn't know we had) and we gave it intramuscularly, while injecting cortisone into the muscles. After that, all we could do was hope. The woman's delirium increased so much during the night that I doubted if she would make it, but the next morning she quieted down and from then on it was just a matter of further medication and constant care. Even so, she couldn't go home for five days. It was the first snakebite I had seen since my uncle Pat had been bitten in Kentucky when I was a child and I had watched Grandpa Turpin save his life by sucking out the venom.

We celebrated our first Sunday at DaMpao with real live electricity. The generator arrived the day before and we installed it after Saturday's clinic session. We also began installing our water pumps to the river, a job that would take several days but was well worth the time and effort. When completed, it would give us plenty of running water for sanitation in the hospital and kitchen.

I went to church at DaMe with H'Klas Sunday morning. The DaMe Alliance Church, run by Christian missionaries, was crowded to the doors. Afterward, I met Maxine Craig, an Alliance missionary nurse, who promised to visit us when she could. We were expecting a nurse of our own any day, but had managed with V.M.O. students while waiting. Not until Maxine came over did I realize how badly we needed one. She did more in five hours than the rest of us could do in a week.

After church services, H'Klas and I stopped in on a few sick villagers and took one, a child with malaria, back to DaMpao with us. The malaria cases in the central highlands were the worst I've ever seen, probably because some people were practically born with it and had had little care or proper medication. Until the American Special Forces came in there had been only makeshift insect control. Prevention of the disease was as mysterious to the people as the cure.

Before leaving DaMe someone at the Villa Alliance remarked that it was too bad we couldn't go to Tournoum.

"Why can't we?" I asked.

"Because it's practically inaccessible," was the reply.

Tournoum was in a valley west of DaLat, on a rugged road hardly more than a path which in places narrowed almost into the jungle itself. Perhaps for no better reason than that I had been told it was almost inaccessible I decided to go there if there was any chance at all of getting through. The missionaries said the road was passable in the dry season, but this was wet midsummer.

"It will be difficult," one said.

"Impossible?" I asked.

He shook his head. "Not impossible. But I wouldn't like to try it at this time of the year."

"Are there many people there?"

"It's a sizable village."

"Any doctor?"

"Witch doctors only."

H'Klas understood enough English to nod when I asked him if he had ever been in Tournoum and if he would like to go back. After clinic a few days later, he and Guy and I drove to DaLat in the Mollie T. We left Guy off in the farmer's market, where he would spend the next couple of hours bargaining for rice, bread, coffee, oil, fish, and fruit, and headed for Tournoum, with H'Klas pointing the way.

We drove west out of DaLat, then found a road so narrow I nearly gave up on the spot. We were at the top of a steep hill, heading into what was hardly more than a trail through thick, green, lush vegetation, part flowers, part jungle, part elephant grass as high as the hood of our Land-Rover. On each side of the road were winding vines, snaking around and between thick-trunked, well-branched trees, with the chirp of monkeys, the squawks and whistles and cries of birds, and the hoarse grunts of wild boar making a perfect setting for a Tarzan picture.

I had to guess where the road was, for most of it was hidden beneath the high grass. Except for patches of tracks here and there, I might as well have been blazing a trail of my own. All I could do was steer the rugged car from patch to patch, assuming that there was road in between. As we descended this winding path, we suddenly came to a steep drop with what was left of the road running parallel to it. As I carefully picked my way along, with the jungle on my right and the cliff on my left, I wondered why I had been so determined to go to Tournoum. What good would I be to Project Concern in the bottom of a gully, crushed beneath the weight of a car? And what good would H'Klas, lying there beside me, be to the people of his village? Moving like a snail, hanging on to the wheel for dear life, peering out through the jungle and the grass for signs of the road, and resisting the temptation to look to my left where potential disaster lay, I edged along until, at last, the road led away from the cliff and down to the bottom of the hill and Tournoum.

We were greeted by scores of frightened, half-dressed, dark-skinned Kohos, the men armed, the women bare-breasted, the children potbellied from hunger. I stopped the car and, as H'Klas started to get out, said, "Ask if we can speak to the chief."

The appearance of one of their own calmed the people down. As H'Klas talked to a man with a Colt .45 pistol strapped to his abdomen and a carbine over his shoulder, I smiled at a big-eyed boy of seven or eight and the child smiled back.

"Chief hunting," H'Klas said. "This number two."

He tapped his head, grinned and pointed at me. "You mean he thinks we were crazy to come?" I said.

We shook hands in the typical Koho fashion, holding our right forearms with our left hands. H'Klas later explained that this kept the evil spirits of one person from entering the body of the other.

H'Klas nodded, then said, "How get back?"

I shrugged, and we both laughed. So did the "number-two" man. He and H'Klas talked a few more minutes, then H'Klas said, "Very sick woman there." He pointed to the circle of thatch-roofed hovels. With "number two" leading the way, we walked over, past a few scrawny chickens which skittered out of the way and a big black sway-backed sow dragging engorged teats through red earth as tiny squealing piglets followed close behind.

"Number two" stopped before a hut, the door of which was a hole about three feet high in the split woven bamboo wall. I ducked into an inferno of dense smoke from two open fires, and tears began streaming from my smarting eyes. As I stood a moment, trying to get used to the acrid odor and the thick fumes, I became vaguely aware that the room was full of people.

"Over there, Bac-Si," H'Klas said.

In one corner of the room a young woman with a new-born infant at her breast was lying on a pallet of boards about a foot off the dirt floor. When I saw blood seeping through a soiled cloth I said, "She's bleeding after delivering her baby."

H'Klas talked to her husband, a handsome, black-eyed youth kneeling beside her, then turned to me and said, "Bleeding since morning. Sorcerer can't stop it."

He helped as I cleaned, cauterized, and bandaged the mother. When I had finished, I said, "Ask if she and her husband will come back to DaMpao with us."

After another exchange, H'Klas said, "His name is Ha'-Chong. He wants to learn."

I nodded. We would take them both back with their baby, the mother for care and minor surgery to remove small bits of placenta that hadn't been properly expelled, the father for instruction. Since we had spent more time with the patient than I intended and no one else in the village was desperately ill, I decided to head back at once so we wouldn't have to risk driving at night.

The return trip to DaLat was nowhere nearly so frightening as the trip out. Aside from the fact that it's safer and easier to drive a powerful car like the Mollie T. uphill than down, it was no longer necessary to pick my way through a constantly disappearing jungle road. All I had to do was follow my own tracks.

On the way to DaLat to pick up Guy before returning to DaMpao, Ha'Chong taught me something I should have been able to figure out for myself. Through H'Klas, I asked him why his people had such smoky fires burning inside their huts. "Because it keeps insects out," was the reply.

Obviously, then, the Kohos did have some knowledge of malaria prevention. At least they knew there was a connection between the disease and the mosquitoes that carried it.

I returned to DaLat the next afternoon to meet Bertha Sanchez and Frank Hooper at the airport. Frank, determined to reach DaMpao as soon as he could, had stayed in Hong Kong only enough to break in a new lab technician there. Bertha was an American nurse of Chinese-Filipino extraction who had gone to Hong Kong as a volunteer. When she learned we were starting a clinic in South Vietnam, she asked to join us there. Since we needed her far more in DaMpao than in Hong Kong, where there were plenty of nurses, we were happy to let her come.

Bertha, small, pretty, and very Oriental in appearance, was actually as American as apple pie. She was born and brought up in California, spoke no Oriental tongue, had been a Girl Scout leader and councilor, and was head nurse of the public schools in San Mateo, near San Francisco. When she first heard about Project Concern, she planned a year ahead to join us for the summer, but didn't have enough money for transportation to Hong Kong and back. She raised it in a typically American way—by asking everyone she knew to help her collect trading stamps.

Getting Bertha Sanchez to Hong Kong became practically a community project in San Mateo during the winter of 1963–1964. Because of her school job, many people knew her and what she wanted to do. Friends, teachers, school children, their parents and relatives, clubs, Girl Scouts, and other organizations gave green stamps to Bertha by the thousands. She kept a careful record of every individual and group who helped her, then, after arriving in Hong Kong, spent much of her spare time on the *Yauh Oi*, where she lived, sending thank-you notes. Still owing about a hundred when she reached DaMpao, she got them all written before she returned home.

Neither she nor Frank wasted a minute getting to work. We had hardly arrived back in DaMpao when a beautiful Vietnamese girl was brought in with pulmonary tuberculosis so severe that there was nothing we could do to save her. Bertha took charge like the truly professional nurse she was, moving quickly to keep the patient comfortable, watching her every minute, giving her the kind of intensive care no one else in the hospital was qualified to give, and freeing me for the dozens of other little jobs that had to be done. Although the girl died before nightfall, the simple fact that we now had a full-time nurse on whom we could depend was a tremendous relief.

Frank, a genius at finding ways of helping that nobody else would ever think of, took over the job of teaching English to the V.M.O. students. He conducted a class that afternoon, and had regular classes thereafter. He set up his laboratory, took charge of the pharmacy, which I had been handling myself, helped Bertha start a system of charts and nursing procedures, and made himself useful all over the camp. Until he and Bertha arrived, Guy and I, living out of suitcases and working only on absolute essentials, were busy day and night. The other two relieved us of so much detail that we were all afforded the luxury of a few hours off to sit around and talk in the evening.

On the night they arrived Bertha and Frank got up from the supper table, said they'd be back soon, and started for the door.

"Where are you going?" I said.

"For a walk," Bertha said. "We always tried to get off the boat in Hong Kong and wander around a bit after supper."

"This isn't Hong Kong," I said. "It's South Vietnam. There's a war on. It's dangerous to go out at night."

"This isn't night," Frank said. "It's still light."

"And we won't go far," Bertha said. "Anyhow, who'll bother us?"

"You just got here," I said. "We don't want to lose you."

"You won't lose us," Frank said. "We'll be back."

I finally let them go, figuring the guard at the gate would stop them. Obviously he didn't, for they were gone almost an hour. By the time they returned, Guy and I were nervous wrecks.

"You can't do this again, Frank," I said. "You'll both be killed."

"There's nothing to worry about," he said.

This was his attitude then, and he never changed. Neither did Bertha. Both ignored the war, acting as if there were no danger, no possibility of ambush or snipers, no lurking enemies, no Viet Cong. They rambled around the country-side for an hour every evening. I stopped objecting after a while because they used the very fact that they hadn't had trouble as proof that they wouldn't. They didn't consider themselves brave or fearless or possessed of any great amount of nerve. Once, when a visitor asked Bertha why she wasn't afraid, she casually said, "Afraid of what?" To her—and to Frank—there was no war.

The patient load increased daily. At first it consisted mostly of Kohos, but soon there were nearly as many Viet-namese. I ignored the animosity between the two races, and insisted that everyone else do the same. I had not come to South Vietnam to treat one race or another. I had come to help anyone needing my help who might accept it. When I learned that the guards on the gate down by the garrison demanded identity cards before letting anyone through, I told them to stop.

"What if Viet Cong try to come in?" asked the lieuten-ant in charge.

"No identity cards," I insisted.

He stopped asking for identity cards, but then posted a guard in front of the hospital. I went back to him and said, "Either take your men away from the hospital itself or I'll move my examining table out in the middle of the road."

He took the guards away, but under protest. Later, Colonel De asked if I wouldn't feel safer with a guard nearer the hospital, but I still didn't think we needed one. I was glad he didn't press the point.

Actually, our relations with the soldiers who protected us were very good indeed. When we began to have movies, they were welcome to bring their families, and we often had some of the men in for dinner. They had few recreational facilities and were glad to accept ours. In return, they occasionally invited us to an animal roast. We accepted when we could, although one day we all made ourselves scarce. During the early afternoon we saw two soldiers coming through the gate with a big brown creature tied upside down by the legs to a pole they carried between them. From where we were it looked like a deer.

"I guess we'll have some venison tonight," Frank remarked.

"Maybe so," I said.

But when the men came closer we saw it was a dog, not a deer. That night none of us even went to the movies, for fear we might have to insult someone by refusing an invitation to a dog roast.

One morning a frail, slender, undernourished youth in the black pajama-like costume of a Vietnamese farmer came in with his wife, a young woman with teeth black from chewing betel nut. His hacking cough and an examination of his chest were all it took to see he had an advanced case of tuberculosis.

"Take him to bed fourteen," I told K'Crah, who was working with me that morning.

Bertha and I spent a good deal of time with him that afternoon, for he was a very sick young man. Neither he nor his wife talked much, but their eyes showed their gratitude, which was enough for me. Even when I told the wife through K'Moung that we couldn't do much for him, she nodded her understanding.

No better the next day, the young man appeared beyond saving. Bertha continued to watch him closely, and, as I frequently stopped by his bed, I thought how his life might have been spared if his illness had been caught in time. Instead of a youth in the physical prime of his life, this was a dying young man.

I felt terribly sorry for him and for his young wife. Right or wrong, I felt no less sorry even after K'Moung came to me and said, "The tuberculosis patient in bed fourteen is Viet Cong."

CHAPTER

14

With school in Hong Kong over for the summer, Mollie prepared to bring the children to DaMpao. Their impending arrival generated an air of expectancy around the hospital compound. Everyone who worked for us, Kohos, Vietnamese, and Westerners alike, looked forward almost as eagerly as I to seeing the family, particularly the children. Some of the Kohos or Vietnamese had never seen a white child, and now they would have four living in their midst.

We rearranged the staff living quarters, converting the women's sleeping area into a big bedroom divided in the middle by a sheet, with four cots for the children on one side and two pushed together into a double bed for Mollie and me on the other. Frank and Guy moved their cots into one corner of the living room. One end of the children's room was partitioned off for Bertha to sleep in, with another cot for Hazel Hunt, who was coming in with Mollie.

When business kept Mollie in Hong Kong longer than

we expected, we decided to let Keith and Pate, the two older boys, come ahead by themselves. Keith was thirteen and Pate eleven. When I met them at the Saigon airport, they appeared to be the two most excited youngsters in South Vietnam. Dressed in identical gray-and-white seersucker jackets, they marched proudly off the airplane like men, then melted into my arms like the kids they were. Guy met us in DaLat, and we got into the Mollie T. to drive to DaMpao.

After we passed a regiment of Vietnamese soldiers, Pate asked, "Who are the Viet Cong, Dad?"

"A large number of people who are very tired of being poor, sick, and hungry, son," I said. "They believe the best way to improve their lives is the Communist way."

"Is it?"

"We don't think so."

"Will we see any Viet Cong, Dad?" Keith asked.

"I doubt it," I said, without conviction. As far as I knew, anyone looking like a Vietnamese could be a Viet Cong.

"Will they come to DaMpao?"

"Of course not."

"Well," Keith said, "if they do, you won't have to worry about us. We'll be good soldiers."

The first thing they saw at DaMpao were the barracks, the protective fences, the lookout towers, the mortar bunkers, and the rifle range, all of which fascinated them. They couldn't wait to change clothes, get my carbine, some shells, and some tin cans for targets, and head back to the rifle range. I had the carbine for protection only in case of direct attack on the hospital and, at the insistence of the garrison commander, kept my aim fairly sharp with occasional target practice. I had a long session that afternoon. The kids kept me there for more than an hour.

Later they had a wonderful time in DaBrach, where they went on a village visit with Bertha, H'Klas, and me. The Kohos lionized them, grinning, nodding, bowing as they crowded around, and the boys loved every minute. We couldn't start the clinic until I said, "Now if you fellows don't mind, we'd like to get cracking."

After supper, which consisted of bread and powdered milk for Keith, since he is a very fussy eater, we talked until bedtime, then I stepped out for a breath of air just in time to meet a truckload of district troops. A young lieutenant jumped out and said, "Viet Cong come here tonight."

"Oh, no," I said.

I watched his men set up .30-caliber machine guns, mortars, and communications equipment, then went to my knees beside the sleeping figures of my sons and prayed, "Not tonight. Please, dear God, not tonight."

Half an hour later there was an alert. While debating whether or not to wake the boys, I saw Frank Hooper calmly playing with Chopper, his pet monkey. I tiptoed over and whispered, "If anything happens, get them up."

Nothing did. A makeshift group of "irregular" Vietnamese soldiers in a nearby village had been mistaken for Viet Cong, triggering what mercifully proved to be a false alarm. But despite the all clear, I had plenty to think about. For the first time since I had reached South Vietnam I was apprehensive. Up to then I had never thought about danger, partly, perhaps, because people like Bertha and Frank refused to concede its existence, but mostly because we were all too busy. Even target practice failed to remind me of the possibility of trouble. I just never believed that the Viet Cong, some of whom we had treated, would attack our hospital. Now I wondered. What if they came when Mollie and the children were there? What could I do to protect them? Was DaMpao really more dangerous than I thought? Was I leading those dearest to me into a trap?

I didn't get much sleep that night. After retiring, I lay for hours in endless debate, weighing the bad against the

143

good, worrying one minute, trying to relax the next. Not until I remembered that we had never had anything but alerts, that all had been false alarms, that the Viet Cong were as eager for the care we could give as the Kohos and the Vietnamese, that we were not an American agency but an international one, that we were there to help anyone who needed help, that as long as we refrained from attacking others nobody would attack us, did I feel easy in having my family with me. I hated the Viet Cong and all it stood for as a military force, but I could not hate a Viet Cong who came to me for medical attention. By the same token, why should the Viet Cong hate me, or do anything to hurt me, or anyone close to me, or anyone who worked with me? Pollyanna reasoning? Perhaps. But that night, with my oldest boys in the next room and my wife and daughter and youngest boy joining us soon, I finally made it make sense to me before falling asleep.

Keith and Pate kept me busy in the next days. I would not let them leave the compound without me, but they went along on village clinic visits, making friends with boys their own age and even learning enough Koho to carry on simple conversations, which was more than I could do. They found an old tree on our grounds and spent hours every day building a tree house with hammers, nails, and some old lumber Guy gave them. They worked a little around the hospital, helping Frank in the pharmacy or doing some small chore for him or Bertha or me. At night they took turns running the movie projector, a job both immensely enjoyed.

Mollie, Scott, and Jan were due in Saigon with Hazel Hunt on a Saturday. Leaving Bertha and Frank in charge at DaMpao, the boys and I drove into DaLat with Guy and hitched a ride to Saigon on an American Air Force C-123. Bill Prowell and Jeff Farrell, who met us at the airport, stayed to help us welcome Mollie, Hazel, and the two little children, then took us to Bill's spacious home for the weekend. Everyone looked wonderful to me, healthy and bubbling over with happiness in our all being together for the first time in nearly two months. We visited the zoo, ate cheeseburgers at the U.S.O., and wallowed in the pampering of Bill's manservant, a smiling, friendly, competent Vietnamese named Ba. Quite a change from the rigors of DaMpao, it served as a short but adequate vacation for me and a chance for us all to enjoy Saigon, at that time still a safe and thoroughly charming city.

We flew back to DaLat Monday morning to find the Lieng Khong airfield bristling with truckloads of more well-armed soldiers than I had ever seen there before. When Captain Jim Stevens of the U.S. Military Advisory Command saw us leave the plane he came right over.

"You'd better take the family into DaLat, Doc," he said. "There are four battalions of Viet Cong rumored in the area, and one of them is supposed to be around DaMpao."

"Four battalions?" I said. "What in the world are they doing here?"

"Maybe it's just a rumor. We're checking it out today and tomorrow. I'll let you know when it's safe to go back. In the meantime, plan to spend the night here."

I wasn't particularly concerned until we were joined later in the day by Bertha, Frank, and Guy. There was nothing unusual about Guy's being in DaLat, but Bertha and Frank were the last people I expected to see there.

"It must be really bad in DaMpao," I said.

"It isn't," Frank said. "Everything's normal. I don't know why they made us leave. It's just another of those false alarms."

"How did they get you and Bertha out?"

"Practically dragged us."

"What about the clinic?"

"No problem. K'Moung and H'Klas will run it in the morning. If they see anyone who might need you, they'll keep him in the hospital until you get there."

While inclined to agree with Frank that the alert was another false alarm, I couldn't stifle new doubts about taking the children into DaMpao. If there was any real danger we wouldn't, of course. On the other hand, it always had been safe, and I found it hard to believe it still wasn't. The rumors of trouble could well have been started by the Viet Cong, who often used rumors to keep people off balance. There were plenty of Viet Cong around DaMpao. They hid out in certain villages by day and traveled by night, but seldom attacked because they were almost always outnumbered by security troops.

They didn't attack this time, either, as we learned the next morning when Major Digger Moravek came over to give us an all clear. It wasn't even they who started the rumors. These began when a large group of self-defense corps had startled the regular Vietnamese army unit in the jungle. Each mistook the other for Viet Cong, resulting in stray shots but no real trouble. Digger told us we were free to leave DaLat whenever we cared to.

Having the family was a mixed blessing. Much as I loved their being with me, I feared more and more for their safety, and constantly wondered if I had done the right thing bringing them to DaMpao. I hired a special night guard to work outside our quarters, and gave everyone in the family strict orders not to leave the house alone after dark. Although none of us on the staff had ever been afraid to go to the outhouse fifty feet from the building at night, I made the family use slop jars so they wouldn't have to go outside. Mollie frequently went on village visits with me, but I let the older boys go only to the nearest settlements, and didn't allow Scott and Jan to leave the compound at all except for occasional trips to DaLat.

The trouble was, I think, that it was impossible to tell Vietnamese from Viet Cong. When I was alone, I never worried about this, but now I thought I saw Viet Cong everywhere. Although I knew our guards were loyal, I began wondering what would prevent a Viet Cong from slipping in unnoticed. I sometimes even imagined that there might be Viet Cong in the night guards we hired from the garrison.

The kids weren't the least bit worried. Jan, who was partial to Oriental men, found a kindred soul in K'Moung. A handsome, compact youth of twenty-three who, while friendly and respectful, had never let his hair down with any of the Westerners on the staff, K'Moung showed a side of himself we never knew existed when he played with Jan, whom he adored. He tickled her, poked at her, played games with her and, beyond everything else, laughed with her as the two found something funny in everything they did together. When they played hide-and-seek, one spotting the other set both off into hysterics. When K'Moung threw a ball to her, it was a signal for more laughter whether she caught it or missed it. They looked for each other every day after clinic, and laughed constantly from the moment they met until the moment they parted.

This little five-year-old daughter of ours actually made an important breakthrough in our relationship with the Kohos and Vietnamese with whom we worked. Until she came along there was always a sense of formality, a touch of shyness, a shell which seemed impossible for us to get through. Perhaps we, too, withheld something of ourselves, setting up barriers of our own which they couldn't get through.

Jan changed all that. Everyone enjoyed watching her and K'Moung together so much that soon we all began to laugh and joke and have fun together. Everything had been too serious for too long. We had all been too formal with each other. Now, with Jan and K'Moung leading the way, we learned to relax. As a direct result of this new feeling of good fellowship, K'Moung organized a volleyball game on the lower field near the barracks. For men only, it soon became the most cosmopolitan pastime in the area, since it brought together staff, soldiers, Kohos, and Vietnamese, all indulging in a fun game cementing comradeship and giving everyone something to talk about and look forward to the next day. It broke down many barriers, including one between Kohos and Vietnamese which had been a constant problem among our V.M.O.'s, some of whom had barely spoken to each other before the volleyball games began.

Jan and Scott, who is a year older, had always played with children on nearby junks in Hong Kong, but there were no Vietnamese children their age around the hospital in DaMpao. The nearest belonged to the security troops, but we didn't want our two youngest going that far alone, so they played together a good deal. Since the compound, with its fences and bunkers and other protective features, resembled a Davy Crockett movie set, cowboys and Indians was a favorite game. We bought Jan a pony for four dollars, which, although she couldn't ride it very far because there was nowhere to go, became an important member of her and Scott's Wild West activities. So did some of the V.M.O.'s, who soon followed K'Moung into Jan's social orbit.

The two little children were busier than their big brothers. After the novelty of being in South Vietnam wore off, Keith and Pate were bored. They spent more and more time around the hospital, not from any special sense of duty but for lack of anything else to do. Pate helped register patients and ran errands. Keith, a budding scientist, liked to work in the lab with Frank, who let him do simple experiments. That was hardly enough to satisfy the youngster. Both he and his brother missed Hong Kong, where they had plenty of friends and more activity than they had time for.

The kids wore shorts and old shirts, with the little ones often getting so dirty they had to change two or three times a day. They wanted to go barefoot, but Mollie made them wear thongs because of the danger of hookworm and snakes. All ate well, although Keith, with his fussy palate, sometimes had to settle for less than the others. Yet, while the living was a bit difficult, the children gained weight in the two months they were there.

One of Mollie's toughest jobs was keeping everyone clean, since she had to wash all our clothes by hand. Even in our early days in Hong Kong she had had access to washing machines, but not in DaMpao. There she couldn't even get hot water. She did the washing in a basin of rain water which she poured from one of several barrels we had put beneath the drains off the roof. We also used rain water for showers. We had rigged up a barrel with pipes that led down to a little shower room where there was a faucet. You could turn it on and off, but you couldn't change the temperature of the water, which was frigid. Frank Hooper was the only one on the staff who really liked it. He went down every night after supper to stand happily under a stream of ice water, but the rest of us jumped in and jumped out. Mollie finally got some of the local people to collect wood and build a small fire under the piped water barrel every four or five days. It didn't give us hot water, but at least it cut the chilling cold, enabling the children to stand it.

When Mollie wasn't busy with domestic chores she worked around the hospital. As the time neared for her return to Hong Kong with the family, I took her with me more and more on village visits. One afternoon she, along with Hazel, Bertha, H'Klas, and a camp employee named H'Doy, drove with me in the Mollie T. to the little Koho community of R'Lom. About five miles from Da-Mpao, this was a typical "new life" hamlet, consisting exclusively of Montagnards rescued from the horrible poverty of the hills where they were born. Having held clinics in a dozen towns like it, I didn't expect anything unusual to happen, even though this was my first visit there.

The trip was uneventful. We drove slowly over the rugged, muddy, bumpy, pock-marked road, through the fringe of the jungle, past rice paddies, villages, animals, and people. The Mollie T., with her blue-and-white markings and the legend, "Project Concern," was now such a familiar sight that almost everyone waved, keeping us all busy waving back. After a squad of Vietnamese soldiers greeted us with their guns high over their heads, Mollie said, "I still don't see how you can tell whether they're Viet Cong or not."

"We always assume that they're not when they wave," I said. "That plus the fact that they're out at all at this time of day is enough to tell us they're friends."

H'Doy, who knew where R'Lom was although he didn't live there, told me to turn into a mucky lane leading to the front gate of the village. As I peered through the windshield, I noticed that a short, slim, ragged, barefooted Koho guard was pointing his gun directly at us, a gesture I considered stupid and uncalled for, since he must have known we were friends. Without thinking, I stopped the car, leaving the motor running, jumped out, and waved H'Doy out with me.

As H'Doy alighted, I said, "Tell that man if he doesn't put the gun down I'll wrap it around his neck."

H'Doy understood nothing except that I was furious that the guard, who couldn't possibly have been Viet Cong, was aiming his gun at us. H'Doy yelled something in Koho, but that seemed to have no effect for the gun remained leveled in my direction. Too angry to worry about the possibilities of the man's meaning business, I continued to walk toward him, shaking my fist and yelling, so mad that I was hardly aware of Mollie calling, "Jim, be careful!" We walked closer and closer, with me yelling and Mollie calling and H'Doy talking and the guard just standing there. Stupid as I thought he was, I was stupider, for if he really meant to shoot me, I made it easier for him with

150

every step I took. But the idea of a Koho guard threatening me with a gun when I had come to help his people was so infuriating that at first I hardly knew what I was doing.

I didn't calm down until I was within fifteen feet of the man, when it suddenly occurred to me that he didn't know who we were or why we had come. Still walking toward him, I said to H'Doy, "Tell him I'm Bac-Si."

H'Doy, who had kept pace with me, talked rapidly in Koho, then the guard wavered. Gradually he lowered the gun, and by the time we reached his side he had it pointed toward the ground. Without smiling or offering his hand, he mumbled something and stepped aside. After yelling back to Mollie to turn off the motor and join us, I stood at the gate with H'Doy to wait for her and the others. When they arrived, we went inside to conduct our clinic in the street.

We might as well have been in the middle of the Ho Chi Minh trail. Few people appeared, and most looked at us with curious expressions which I couldn't interpret as distaste, fright, or suspicion. There were only two patients, both with what seemed to be tuberculosis, but neither stayed still long enough for proper examinations. A young man approached H'Klas and talked several minutes with him.

"He wants to study," H'Klas said.

Delighted to find a V.M.O. candidate in such an unlikely place, I said, "Tell him we'll take him back. We can make room for him."

The youth shook his head.

"He thinks it would be better to come later," H'Klas said.

"Tell him we'll be glad to see him whenever he comes," I said.

They talked a few more minutes, then the young man moved off. After he left, H'Klas kept looking furtively around and finally said, "Bac-Si, we go."

On the way back to DaMpao he and H'Doy talked at great length. Not until we got back to the hospital did I learn that R'Lom was alive with Viet Cong sleeping in the huts. The villagers let them stay because the Viet Cong bribed them with food and gifts.

A week later I flew to Saigon with Mollie and the kids. Much as I hated to see them leave, I breathed a long sigh of relief as I watched their plane take off for Hong Kong.

CHAPTER

15

Frank Hooper stood in front of a class of Village Medical Officer candidates, and read slowly from Dr. Jack Lange's *Physicians' Handbook*.

"Symptoms?" he said, his voice rising into a question. He repeated it, this time in syllables: "Symp—toms?" Then he turned his back on the class and wrote the word on a portable blackboard, carefully printing it in block letters in the upper left corner. He spelled it out in English, the language we wanted the V.M.O.'s to use, for this made the teaching easier and eventually would make the learning easier. All the students were learning English faster than we could learn Koho. They wrote "symptoms" on their pads, then Frank went on.

"Fever," he said. "Fe—ver." He wrote it beneath "symptoms" on the blackboard, and dark heads bent over pads, carefully copying the letters.

"Shaking chills," Frank said. "Shak—ing chills." Then: "No appetite. No ap—pe—tite." Then: "Aching all over. Ach—ing all o—ver."

He waited until everyone had completed the column

beneath "symptoms," and moved on to the next step. Using the same questioning inflection as before, he said, "Diagnosis?" After repeating it syllable by syllable, he turned and wrote it in the upper center part of the blackboard beside "symptoms."

He faced the class again and, this time without seeming to ask a question, he said in positive tones, "Malaria. Ma—la—ri—a." Before returning to the blackboard, he added, "Caused by bite of mosquito. Kill mosquito, no malaria." As he wrote all this on the board beneath "malaria," the students carefully traced the words on their pads. When all were finished, Frank said, again in the rising inflections of a question, "Treatment?" After repeating that, he printed "treatment" in the upper right corner of the blackboard.

Finally, positive again, he slowly said, and repeated in syllables, "Chloroquin." After getting that down on the blackboard, he gave the dosages for various ages, then invited questions. A few of the students asked him to repeat some of the information, but most had it all the first time around.

"I have told you today," he said. "You must learn, then soon you will tell me—understand?"

Everyone nodded. These future V.M.O.'s knew that at examination time at the end of the month we would ask questions based on the day's lesson, and on the lessons of all the other days. The students who passed would be given white jackets with the blue Project Concern insignia, and graduate to the next step of the three-month program—a month of intensive work in the Tuyen Duc provincial hospital in DaLat. Those successful there would return to DaMpao for the last month of instruction from us. After that they would go home to their villages equipped to diagnose and treat about 90 per cent of the illnesses to which Kohos and Vietnamese in the central highlands are most susceptible.

To an American familiar with the long, painful road to a medical degree or a nursing certificate, this sounds like a ridiculously simple program to reach a complicated goal, and of course it is. Our V.M.O.'s are not expected to be doctors or nurses or diagnosticians in the true sense of the word. They hardly approach the knowledge even of an army medic, who must know how to handle any emergency in combat situations. In order to know how a V.M.O. with only a few months of instruction can run a village clinic, it is necessary to know something about the Koho villages of South Vietnam and the diseases the people in them are most likely to contract.

Until we opened our hospital in DaMpao, these people had no idea what made them sick or what possible cures might be available. They knew nothing about cleanliness, personal hygiene, or the dangers of contagion. They knew nothing about medicine, drugs, shots, pills, or any of the other appurtenances of ordinary medical practice. The illnesses suffered by nine out of every ten of the Koho villagers were either easily preventible or easily treated. The tenth would need a real doctor.

The most common ailments of the central highlands people are malaria, deficiency conditions caused by starvation or unbalanced diet, intestinal parasites, and minor infections. I selected thirteen drugs available from the South Vietnamese government medical stores, including piperazine for intestinal parasites, chloroquin for malaria, Vitamin B and iron tablets for the deficiency states, and sulfa for the minor infections. If we taught the V.M.O.'s to recognize these common ailments so they could administer the proper drugs, it wouldn't matter whether we were there or not. They could get along without us, without doctors or nurses or the hospital. Naturally, if they encountered a serious disease with which they were not trained to cope, they would not be able to cure, or perhaps even to treat it, but these cases would be the exception, not the rule. It would be far from an ideal situation, of course, but certainly better than nothing. Since, because of South Vietnam's unsettled conditions we didn't know how long we could stay there, it was essential that local people have some knowledge of medicine, no matter how skimpy.

South Vietnam was altogether different from Hong Kong, which had a constantly increasing pool of trained personnel. That was why I could leave Hong Kong—doctors, nurses, and medical technicians were streaming in there from Red China by the score. Needing jobs, not training, they were on every hospital and medical facility waiting list in the colony, including ours. The South Vietnamese, having no such pool, were in desperate need of whatever medical training they could get.

Dr. Phan, the chief medical officer of Tuyen Duc province, well aware of the circumstances and glad to cooperate with us, made it possible for our students to spend a month at the government hospital in DaLat as part of their V.M.O. training course. We decided it should be the middle month of the program because they would be lost in the hospital the first month and might find it difficult to readjust to village life if it were after the third. We also felt it would be easier for them to learn the first rudiments from us, then return to us for further instruction after a month at the hospital. Service in the government hospital had the added advantage of proving to our students that it really was a place where sick people were treated and often cured. The Koho had always been afraid of the hospital. V.M.O.'s, returning to their people with news of surgical triumphs and the recovery of good health, could establish confidence in doctors and hospital procedure among villagers fearful of both.

The first key to success in our V.M.O. program was K'Moung because he was the only medically trained Koho in the area. He had learned the fundamentals we wanted to teach from American Army medicos when the Special

Forces had occupied the DaMpao facility that Project Concern took over. Having learned more English than the others, K'Moung was also our bridge to the villagers, for it was through him that we could best communicate. K'Moung worked closely with Goff Gapp when the V.M.O. program began a few weeks before my arrival in DaMpao, later became my right-hand man, and would, I'm sure, keep the program alive if the Westerners were forced to leave.

With the help of the village chiefs who appointed them, K'Moung brought in the first V.M.O. candidates from surrounding Montagnard villages, so Goff's original group of students was made up exclusively of K'Moung's Koho contacts. They were short, compact, handsome, finely-featured men who looked alike at first glance only because we knew so little about them. K'Moung himself was the most impressive, partly, perhaps, because his English was most fluent and he had obvious qualities of leadership. About five feet six inches tall, he was slender and graceful in movement and confident in manner. A friendly man with a constant smile playing about his lips, there was from the beginning a strong hint of the warmth he later displayed toward Jan.

The most promising member of Goff's first class was H'Klas. About an inch taller than K'Moung, H'Klas, with his thin face, full, wavy jet-black hair and large dark-brown eyes, looked exactly like a Polynesian. Although he knew just a little English and was very shy at first, it soon became evident that he was unusually bright. He had such a quick grasp of everything we taught him that I felt he should be given the opportunity for more formal instruction. He had had enough schooling to make it possible for us to enter him in high school in DaLat, and he is now well on his way to completing his secondary education. Although he no longer has time to work actively with Project Concern, we have granted him a small scholarship allowance, and I have a crazy dream of someday finding a way to send him to the United States for advanced study leading to a medical degree. At the moment this is more wild wish than realistic plan.

K'Bran, another of the original V.M.O. students, is the son of a Protestant preacher in the village of DaBrach, which is hardly a mile from DaMpao. One night DaBrach was invaded by the Viet Cong, who cut down the fences and demanded the use of the village for a local headquarters, but K'Bran's father and the village chief flatly refused. After a harrowing night of threats, arguments and gun brandishing, the Viet Cong left without firing a shot and, to the best of my knowledge, never came back.

The most muscular member of the group was K'Krah, a heavy-set youth with bright green eyes who, although ill at ease, found it easier than most of the others to relax in our presence. He was also the only one who seemed able to look any of us in the eye without turning away. Americans tend to distrust people who refuse to make eye-to-eye contact, but the Kohos' failure to do so was simply a reflection of their shyness. K'Krah, outgoing and friendly, later became the star of the volleyball games K'Moung started after Jan came to DaMpao. He came from the village of Riento.

Probably the shyest and most reserved member of our first V.M.O. class was K'Crai, whose home was R'Lom. He seemed afraid of his own shadow, insecure, and terribly unsure of himself, but I soon discovered that he was a hard, willing worker who was interested in learning as much as he could. Not so quick as H'Klas, nor so confident as K'Moung, nor so outgoing as K'Chai, he had dogged determination and tremendous dedication which helped overcome his lack of self-confidence.

The only woman in the first class was K'Srang, a beautiful young Koho from DaMe. The girls of South Vietnam are lovely, and the Montagnard girls especially so. K'Srang had the delicate features of her Polynesian forebears—huge dark eyes, silky black hair, very red lips, and soft, smooth olive skin. Bright, quick, and completely dedicated, she worked hard, spending long hours in the hospital. She became devoted to Bertha Sanchez, the first Western nurse to join us in DaMpao, following Bertha everywhere and asking her endless questions.

Since we were in predominantly Koho country, I hardly expected to find many Vietnamese in the area. But right from the beginning, Vietnamese came to the hospital for treatment, and shortly after we opened our V.M.O. program we accepted a Vietnamese student. On the day he arrived, H'Klas, obviously upset, came to me and said, "Bac-Si, we will not work with the Vietnamese."

I was stunned. "What do you mean?" I demanded.

Groping for words, H'Klas said, "Fifty years ago, Bac-Si, the French in Saigon sent men here to Tuyen Duc province to capture a *moi*."

"*Moi*? That's French for 'me.'"

He shook his head. "No," he said. "*Moi* means savage —monkey—ape. They wanted a *moi* to take back to France and show in the zoo in Paris."

"There are apes here," I said.

"You don't understand, Bac-Si. They wanted a *savage*." He pointed to himself. "We—Kohos—were the savages they came for. They wanted to capture us because they heard we had tails. And we have lived with this name *moi* ever since. The Vietnamese don't like us and we don't like them. That's why we will not work with them."

As we talked, other V.M.O. students gathered behind him. They stared at me, their lips set in hard lines, their eyes like coals. I turned to K'Moung, who seemed as agitated as the rest, and asked, "Do you know why I came here?" Without waiting for an answer, I said, "I came because I learned you had no doctor when you were sick. I came because I wanted to try to make your sick well, and to teach you to make your sick well. Do you think I cared what you were, who you were, or what others called you? Do you think I cared whether you were white or black, Koho or Vietnamese, French or Chinese?"

I spoke very slowly, stopping often to give K'Moung time to translate, and watching carefully for reactions. "The Vietnamese once called you *moi*—perhaps some still do. You know and I know that you are not *moi*. So do the Vietnamese who come to the hospital. And so will the Vietnamese who want to learn what we are trying to teach you. They have sick people in their villages, too, sick people we want to help. Are you going to refuse them the chance because their ancestors thought you had tails? Are you going to call a man bad because he is Vietnamese? Are you going to want him to call you *moi* forever?"

The students shifted their feet, and the fire left their eyes. "I am going to accept this Vietnamese who wants to learn what you are learning. You are going to accept him, too. He doesn't call you *moi* or think of you as *moi*. He will call you *friend*, and that's what you will call him. And we will all work together, Koho and Vietnamese alike, to help make sick people well. Do you understand?"

When K'Moung finished the translation, the anger was replaced by sheepish embarrassment, and the group broke up. I didn't expect to wipe out fifty years of suspicion and hatred in one talk, and of course it didn't happen. But the Kohos accepted the Vietnamese as a fellow student, just as they accepted Vietnamese whom we took in as V.M.O. candidates later. And at least in some cases actual friendships did spring up, for on picnics and swimming parties to the river some Kohos and Vietnamese walked hand in hand in obvious good fellowship. Since those first days our proportion of students has been about four to one in favor of Kohos, with not one racial problem ever again developing.

Frank Hooper, who did everything else so well, was the

bellwether of our faculty. Besides helping me with the medical lectures, he broke in new students in simple hospital procedure, such as applying already prescribed medication, cleaning skin lesions, putting on bandages, taking temperatures, and many of the other thousand-and-one things medical aides must know. Having organized the pharmacy, he taught V.M.O. candidates how to read and fill prescriptions, how to count out pills, and how to tell one basic drug from another.

One of our most important jobs was teaching the students something about public health, the subject I had flunked the first time I tried for my British license. During their three-month course, they had to learn all we could teach them of elementary sanitation, how to dig wells, how to build privies, how to understand the association between malaria and the mosquito, and the association between the feces and hookworm. We wanted them to know the life cycle of the most common parasites, what we call preventive medicine. That, in fact, was the first question we asked our students when they took final examinations— "What is preventive medicine?" We then required them to give five examples of how they could participate in preventive medicine in their own villages.

Part of the third month's curriculum was going with me on village visits. I tried as far as possible to take the V.M.O. student to his home village. K'Crai went to R'Lom with us, K'Bran to DaBrach, K'Krah to Psourr or Riento, K'Srang to DaMe. This helped not only the student but the villagers, too, because it proved to them that one of their own people now really knew something about the process of making them well when they were sick, and gave them confidence in him.

We had ten students in our first class, but three dropped out when they failed to pass the examination after the first month. I debated a long time before letting them go, but they so obviously were lost there was no point in keeping them. They were free to continue to work at the hospital, of course, and a couple of them stayed, but it would have been pointless to send them on to DaLat for the second month of training under Dr. Phan at the provincial hospital. However, we determinted to keep those who passed the first month's examination because we knew if they could go that far they would eventually be able to finish.

We had a regular graduation exercise for the seven who completed the course. The South Vietnamese government in Saigon cooperated, as did the Tuyen Duc provincial government in DaLat. Each student received a diploma with the official stamp of the administration in Saigon and signed by the Minister of Health, as well as by Dr. Phan and me. Dr. Phan, Colonel De, and I all spoke, and each graduate received a stethoscope, a thermometer, sterile dressings, and a box of medicine that included such drugs as sulfa, chloroquin, liquid sulfa, piperazine, deficiency tablets, benzyl benzoate, and aspirin.

The V.M.O.'s received no further title, but their diplomas designated them as Village Medical Officers trained by Project Concern. As a matter of courtesy, we continued to address them as "Mister" or "Miss" rather than by their names with no title. This gave them a sense of self-respect and confidence, all so necessary in the work they would be performing among their own people.

Graduation was a simple but deeply impressive ceremony. When it ended, I watched with growing pride as Colonel De and the other honored guests from DaLat and surrounding villages congratulated them. Each V.M.O. shook hands firmly as he looked eagerly into the eyes of the person addressing him. As I met each pair of eyes when my turn came, I remembered the day three months before when all I had encountered was a head bowed in shyness and eyes that refused to look into mine, and I thought, "Perhaps we are doing something really worth while."

I was sure of it when I glanced over at our new stu-

dents, the "freshmen" we had just recruited for the next
V.M.O. class. Their eyes were down, their heads averted,
and they were thoroughly ill at ease. There were the
K'Chais and the K'Crais, the K'Brans and the H'Klases,
the new generation of Project Concern V.M.O.'s I was
pleased to see that some were Vietnamese future students
also and that the Kohos among them didn't seem to mind.

CHAPTER

16

It was late August, time for Bertha Sanchez and Hazel
Hunt to return to the States. Both had become so much a
part of our team in DaMpao that I had almost forgotten
they had important jobs back home, and that when they
left we would have to find replacements for them. The
V.M.O.'s could help around the hospital, of course, but it
would take three of them all day to do what Bertha could
do in one morning. Hazel, although not a nurse, had helped
organize registration of patients, kept their records in shape,
and handled dozens of other chores. The hospital was growing and we needed help. Instead, we were about to lose two
people who had become almost indispensable.

"I wish I knew where to find a couple of experienced
Western nurses," I said to Frank one night.

"Maybe somebody will come in from Hong Kong," he
suggested.

"I hate to ask anyone to come here," I said. "It might be
inconvenient to accept and embarrassing to refuse. The
only way really to get people is by accident. All we can do
is hope somebody reads about us somewhere and just
decides to come."

I didn't know it, but two young nurses, Ann Kidder and Lynn Allen, had already read about us. The girls had picked up a Project Concern folder in the Bangkok airport while waiting to change planes en route to the States from Laos, where they had worked nearly a year at the Tom Dooley hospital. As she told me later, Ann said, "That folder talked directly to us. We got on the telephone and called Bill Prowell in Saigon. He told us to come ahead."

So it happened that Bill, who had already done so much for Project Concern, now acquired two American nurses at a time when we needed them most. The girls canceled their flights home, went to Saigon, talked to Bill, and soon were on one of those hot, sticky little Air Vietnam DC-3's to DaLat. Guy Brehon met them in the Mollie T. and drove them to DaMpao where all of us, including Bertha and Hazel, greeted them with open arms.

Ann was from the Chicago suburb of Naperville and Lynn from New York. I guess our folder in the Bangkok airport ruined all their good intentions to go home. Besides, as Lynn put it, the girls "really never got Asia quite out of our systems." We offered them one other attraction—we were new, and our pioneering features attracted them. We could pay them only a hundred and fifty dollars a month, but this didn't bother them. No one ever expected to make a fortune working for Project Concern.

Ann developed a warm affection for the Montagnard people, and they for her. Soon she was thinking up little things to help them, to entertain them, and to educate them. She sent home to the States for square-dance records, but we didn't have a record player so we had them taped. Then she taught the V.M.O.'s square dancing, which they called "cowboy dancing." Night after night we had square dancing in the main hall, with Ann calling out the figures, and everyone had a wonderful time.

The Kohos loved anything relating to cowboys. When we showed the film, *Seven Brides for Seven Brothers*, they particularly liked a scene in which the seven brothers went into the town to pick up their girls and take them back to their mountain retreat. In the picture, they went behind the house of a girl they wanted and meowed like a kitten, and when the girl came out to see what was going on, they kidnaped her, For months after that the V.M.O.'s went all over the compound meowing at Ann.

She set up a mail-order system, sending orders to Sears, Roebuck for cowboy equipment, and soon parcels came in by the dozen with blue jeans, cowboy belts, cowboy hats and shirts, and just about everything but boots and horses. Ann paid for them by American check, then sold them at less than cost to the V.M.O.'s for piastres. Pretty soon she had the biggest collection of piastres in DaMpao. With the rate of exchange so much in favor of the American dollar, she was sure to lose when she got ready to go home.

Not long after Ann and Lynn arrived Bill Prowell and Jeff Farrell sent us Marie Harding, a lovely young graduate of Sarah Lawrence College. Marie (or "Maurie," as she pronounced it) was an artist from New York who heard about us when she stopped in Saigon on her way around the world. A girl of considerable means and great personal charm, she came as a volunteer, and soon had picked up the work that Hazel Hunt had been doing, helping with registration and records, and making herself useful in many other ways.

At about the time Marie appeared, a brilliant young Harvard Business School graduate named John Allen came to DaMpao. John was an organizational genius who drew plans for hospital improvements, set up charts to help us keep track of everything from villages and V.M.O.'s to the best locations for privies, and once even went with me to Cheo Rio to survey a site for a hospital we thought of opening there. (We postponed the idea because of a lack of funds.)

Marie and John were in DaMpao only a few months, but that was long enough for them to fall in love. At their request I performed the marriage, which I could do as an ordained Methodist minister. We had the wedding right at DaMpao, with Frank Hooper serving as best man, Lynn and Ann as bridesmaids, and the rest of the hospital personnel and ambulatory patients as witnesses. Everyone, including the principals, was back at work before the day ended.

Frank, who loved all living things, had a particularly soft spot in his heart for birds and animals. When he left Hong Kong to go to DaMpao, he told Dorothy Plant that he'd bring back a baby elephant, a baby tiger, and a monkey. He still talks about getting an elephant, but he gave up the idea of a tiger because a tiger terrified one of the surrounding villages and finally carried off a child, whose bones were later found in the jungle. Another tiger haunted the Special Forces camp at Phey Srung, every so often taking a cow or a calf from a corral they kept there. The men built a hunting platform but didn't have time for a twenty-four-hour guard. The tiger waited until it was unmanned, then went into the corral and made himself at home. Frank always said he'd like an animal that smart, but not one that predatory. He settled for Chopper, the monkey, which was brought in by some Kohos who found her in a tree after his mother had been eaten by a pack of wild dogs. Chopper, devoted to Frank, eventually returned to Hong Kong with him, where he now lives happily with all the other birds and beasts in Dorothy's menagerie.

I've seen great eaters, but never one in a class with Frank. He has the most fantastic appetite I've ever heard of, yet looks as if he were starving to death. His narrow shoulders, long, thin nose, horn-rimmed glasses, and skinny frame make him appear a candidate for one of our hospital beds, yet he eats so much that we tease him about his tapeworm, which we called George. The gag started in Hong Kong and followed Frank to DaMpao, where Monsieur Tom, the chef, prepared two extra-big meals at each sitting, "one for Frank and one for George."

One day Sergeant Takahara of the American Special Forces brought in a twelve-year-old Vietnamese boy named Ha and asked if we could take care of him. Ha was an abandoned child whom the sergeant had found sleeping in a barroom in DaLat. He took Ha back to Phey Srung, but there were no facilities there for a boy so young, so he brought Ha to us. We gave Ha clothes, a place to sleep, three meals a day, and arranged for him to go to Father Vallencort's little Catholic school. Ha became something of a local pet until he began to give us trouble. He skipped school and took other boys out with him. One day we caught him rolling dice with Monsieur Tom in the kitchen. When we traced several unfortunate occurrences around the compound to Ha, we tried to place him elsewhere. Guy and Loc, a Vietnamese who works in our Saigon office, hoped to enter him in a training school there, but they demanded a birth certificate, which Ha didn't have and couldn't get. We later found out the real reason they wouldn't take him was their fear that he might be a Viet Cong agent, which was not so ridiculous as it sounds. The Viet Cong use many youngsters Ha's age for that purpose. But Ha was no Viet Cong agent, only a boy who wouldn't behave. At this writing he is still at DaMpao and still a problem because we don't know what to do with him. We just can't give up completely and turn him loose to starve emotionally or even physically. All we can do is hope that sooner or later he will straighten out.

Although at first we had more deaths at DaMpao than Hong Kong, we later leveled off and went for more than two months in the autumn of 1964 without a single one. But in December a sudden rush of desperately ill patients threatened that record and put us all on twenty-four-hour duty. There was K'Seo, suffering from an advanced case of tuberculosis with attendant respiratory complications. There was a hydrocephalic boy with a head the size of a basketball. There was an infant girl with an extreme case of tetanus of the newborn. A Vietnamese teenager with meningitis arrived in a semi-conscious condition which soon developed into a deep stupor and total unresponsiveness. A young Koho village chief was bleeding from a peptic ulcer. A Montagnard soldier, victim of the deadly combination of malaria and cholera, was airlifted by helicopter from Phey Srung. A Vietnamese farmer with stomach pains turned out to have extensive cancer with metastasis to vital organs. A woman from Tung Nghia had a goiter with a large, deep abscess. On top of all this, D'Gle, K'Moung's young wife and a member of our own staff family, was expecting her first baby any day.

K'Seo, the first of the seriously sick to be brought in, was everybody's project, for he lasted a long time and became almost a symbol of success or failure. Day after day we worked on him, not leaving him alone for a minute. We put a Levine tube into his stomach and a catheter into his urinary tract. We took turns suctioning off thick mucus from his throat, giving him intramuscular penicillin, flushing ground sulfa pills through the Levine tube, dosing him with chloramphenicol, irrigating his catheter, carefully measuring and recording his fluid intake and output.

"How can we give so much time and so much care and so much medicine to this patient?" asked K'Moung one night as he worked on K'Seo's chart. "He is only one person."

"If that one person were you or a loved one, would you understand?" I said. He nodded, and went on with his charting.

Despite all the time and care and medication, K'Seo died on his nineteenth day in the hospital. He seemed to rally a bit just before the end, giving us real hope, then he sank rapidly. His death affected us all, including every one of the

V.M.O.'s, for there wasn't a student or member of the staff who hadn't taken part in the long, futile fight to save him. My immediate reaction was self-condemnation, for it seemed I must have made some error of commission or omission, but I later realized on thinking it over that K'Seo's case had been pretty hopeless right from the beginning. Considering our limited equipment, we had been lucky to keep him alive so long.

His death was the first of four within twenty-four hours. The teenage girl with meningitis never had a chance. She died twelve hours after we admitted her. The chief with the peptic ulcer bled out during the night. Although his hopes were slim, I felt we might have done something with blood and plasma, and was very much upset that we were out of both when he came in. The last to go that night was the little hydrocephalic, who lived only three days after we first saw him. The Montagnard soldier from Phrey Srung lasted a week, but there was nothing we could do for him either.

The night I learned the farmer had cancer I brought K'Moung over to help me tell his wife. We waited until the man was asleep so he would not see her reaction, and I said, "Your husband is very sick."

She knew from our manner and the tone of our voices that he would die. "How long?" she asked through K'-Moung.

"A few months," I said. "Do you want to stay here or take him home?"

Two big tears rolled down her cheeks. She sighed, then said, "I will take him home in the morning."

Twice that night I walked past her trying to sleep bent into a sitting position over the legs of her husband. The first time she paid no attention to me. The second, she roused briefly, and in the light of the flickering oil lamp beside the bed I could see a wan smile on her tear-streaked face. I think she wanted to show me she appreciated us.

To help the woman with the abscessed goiter, I had to hurt her as I plunged a curved clamp deep into the infected mass. We had warned her, and she held tightly to her husband's hands during the procedure, crying out once, but otherwise accepting the excruciating pain with dignity. Later, when I paused by her bed, she reached up, grasped my arm and squeezed it, and I knew she had forgiven me. Hers was one story that ended happily. She was soon able to go home, well on the way to recovery. So could the infant with tetanus.

D'Gle's delivery was uneventful. She had a healthy baby girl, whose sudden cry split the stillness death had left. Aroused patients and their families smiled at each other, more comfortable, perhaps, in the knowledge that new life was here, too. When Ann handed the child to her beaming father, K'Moung cradled her in his arms a moment. After handing her back to the nurse, he turned to me and said, "It is good to know my wife will not have to go back to the fields tomorrow as my mother did the day after I was born."

A few days before Christmas we had word that Captain An, the district chief, wanted to see H'Klas in his headquarters at Lieng Khang airfield in DaLat. As chief of five "new life" Koho villages, H'Klas had been an important figure in the area, but he could help his people far more with a proper medical education. Captain An's desire to see him could mean only one thing—that he wanted H'Klas back in the village complex. When Frank and I drove H'Klas over to the airfield, the captain confirmed our fears.

"Captain An," I said, "I must beg you not to take H'Klas back."

"Why?"

"Because he has the talent to become a fine doctor."

"There are no Koho doctors."

"H'Klas could be the first."

"His people need him."

"They will need him more as a doctor than as a chief."

"Why can't you take someone else?"

"Because," I said, "of all our V.M.O.'s, H'Klas has the best qualifications to go to America if we can find a way to send him there. He must go to college someday, and to medical school, and he must return a doctor, the first doctor of his people."

Captain An lowered his head, rubbed his chin, and thought for several minutes. He finally looked up and said, "All right, Bac-Si. I give this man to you."

"To his people," I said.

"To his people."

"You will not regret this, Captain."

On the way back in the Mollie T. Frank said, "I'm glad, Mr. H'Klas—very glad that you will be allowed to work with Project Concern, and to study and perhaps someday to become a doctor."

"I rejoice, too, Frank," H'Klas said.

Now Christmas was only three days off. The V.C. announced five heads would decorate poles in a nearby village to celebrate a holiday that meant as much to Vietnamese Christians as to Western Christians. They didn't specify which village or whose heads. We paid no attention to the threat. Like rumors, threats were used by the Viet Cong as a means of keeping the villagers' nerves on edge.

The Plummers, old friends of my family in Ashland, Kentucky, sent me a hundred dollars to use for the staff. We raised a few more dollars among the Westerners until we had enough to buy every V.M.O.—there were nearly forty—a knitted sweater in Project Concern's deep blue, with a small white "P.C." in the lower left side. We could buy the sweaters in DaLat for three and a half dollars apiece.

On December 23 Dorothy Plant arrived from Hong Kong with Pearl Whitting, a Korean-American who was to become manager of our DaLat office. They brought a trunkload of gifts, including several boxes sent by Bertha from San Francisco, Christmas decorations, and dried foods for Christmas-dinner trimmings. They helped Marie, Lynn, and Ann fix up the dining room with a huge tree, complete with streamers and balls and angel hair and tinsel and colored lights. K'Moung and K'Chai made a large, delicately lovely illuminated Christmas star of paper and cardboard, a traditional Vietnamese Christmas ornament, which bore the legend: "Project Concern."

V.M.O.'s from about twenty-five villages came back to the hospital for a Christmas Eve celebration. Through some legerdemain he had learned in his army days, Larry Wiesner scrounged one of the biggest hogs I've ever seen from a nearby agricultural experimental station, and Monsieur Tom barbecued it. Guy Brehon climbed into a special Santa Claus outfit popular in Southeast Asia (it has a long red skirt instead of trousers), and handed gifts to everybody. Koho and Vietnamese alike laughed, sang, played games, and fraternized until about eleven, when we heard shouting and the noise of heavy trucks.

I rushed out to find a group of fifty crack rangers from the Phey Srung Special Forces camp led by Captain Vincent Triano.

"Vince," I yelled, as he dismounted from a weapons carrier, "what are you doing here?"

"We heard the Viet Cong threatened to cut off a few heads," he said. "We just want to make sure one of them isn't yours."

"Thanks," I said. "They haven't come around yet."

"Things are quiet up our way," Vince said. "I think we'll just stick around until after Christmas. We don't want anything to happen to you."

On Christmas Day we made the rounds of our in-patients but had no clinic. Dorothy spent the whole morning fixing up the dinner she had brought from Hong Kong. We made a family affair of it in the house where we slept, then joined the others in the big dining room. At midafternoon a young man from one of the nearby villages asked if I would go with him to see his wife, who had just given birth to a baby daughter. Frank and I took him back in the Mollie T., leaving the girls to continue to enjoy themselves at the Christmas party. The new mother was in some pain, but there was nothing seriously wrong with her. We reassured her and her husband, left medication with them, and started back to DaMpao. We talked most of the way, then, hearing the sounds of Christmas music, fell silent as we approached the hospital.

"O, come, all ye faithful . . ."

I stopped the Mollie T. and turned off the noisy motor. For fifteen minutes we sat, wrapped in our own thoughts. I wondered how Mollie was celebrating, and my heart ached with loneliness for her and for Keith and for Pate and for Jan and for Scott, while from above the voices of men and women from opposite ends of the earth joined in the old songs which meant so much. I swallowed a lump and turned my head away so Frank wouldn't see the tears in my eyes.

After a while he tapped me gently on the shoulder.

"Merry Christmas, Jim," he said softly.

"Merry Christmas, Frank," I murmured.

Then I turned the key in the Mollie T., started the motor, and continued on up the hill.

CHAPTER
17

One morning at clinic I had just completed a minor plastic-surgery procedure on a Vietnamese soldier with an old bayonet wound of the forehead when Mr. K'Man, who was registering patients with Miss K'Mum that morning, stopped me and said, "Very sick child in your room, Bac-Si. Dying."

I brushed aside the gaily-flowered curtain that served as a door for my office and was greeted by a tormented young Vietnamese mother with tears running down her face. Close in her arms she held a screaming boy with a small, black, round skullcap on his head. The cap, embroidered with red, yellow, and green threads, is worn by Vietnamese boys between the ages of one and four.

"She says the boy is dying," H'Klas told me. "She says he has been seized by evil spirits the sorcerer in Nam San village cannot shake loose."

The boy, squirming and howling from pain, arched his back, turning his head toward me at the same time. His features were hideously distorted by the largest facial abscess I have ever seen, almost completely closing his right eye, making his right ear jut out, and erasing the normal ridge on the right side of his nose.

"Take him into the minor surgery room, Mr. H'Klas," I said. "Quickly."

H'Klas reached for the child, but the mother tightened her grip on him.

"Tell her we can help if she will let us," I said.

H'Klas spoke in the melodious high-pitched Vietnamese warble he knew as well as his own monotoned Koho tongue. She looked at him doubtfully for a moment, then reluctantly released her hold. Gently, H'Klas carried the boy after me into minor surgery. The mother started to follow, but he reassured her again with a few words, and she stayed behind.

Carefully avoiding nerves and major blood vessels, I made deep multiple incisions about the right side of the face, and a cupful of foul green-yellow purulent fluid cascaded into an emesis basin held by H'Klas. The boy's screams subsided as we put in drains, a dressing, and a huge dose of an antibiotic. By the time we brought him back to his mother, who was sitting on the edge of a cot in the ward we had assigned her, he was fast asleep.

"He will be all right," I said. "We have taken him to the 'spirit separating room,' and all the evil spirits are gone."

When H'Klas translated, she smiled. I smiled back, thankful for my inspiration in using the term "spirit separating room." I could as well have called it the "sorcerer's separating room," for one of our biggest problems at DaMpao was to get the people to bring us their sick before going to the sorcerers instead of afterward. The little boy I had operated on obviously had had a small abscess that could easily have been treated in the clinic if we had seen him in time. Instead, his family had taken him to the village sorcerer, who couldn't cope with a condition that grew progressively worse when not properly treated.

Not that I underestimate the power of sorcery. Some of the sorcerers' methods down through the years have carried more than a grain of effectiveness. In England they once hanged witches or burned them at the stake for treating a king with the leaves of the foxglove for his dropsy. Today we treat congestive heart failure with digitalis, which was first extracted from foxglove. For centuries sorcerers and witch doctors have used snakeroot for people with the symptoms of high blood pressure. Recently Western medicine has discovered that a derivative, rauwolfia serpentina, is tremendously effective in driving down blood pressure. In the central highlands of South Vietnam the sorcerers use one plant—I never found out which one—that is pretty good for diarrhea. So when it comes to sorcerers, you must, while recognizing their limitations, keep a fairly open mind.

The sorcerers in the central highlands capitalize on the fact that the Montagnards and Vietnamese are largely spirit worshipers. The people accept the sorcerers' prayers —to the house, to the stream, to the sky, or whatever—as gospel. These prayers, which cost a certain amount, are the first step in the sorcerers' fight against illness. If this doesn't work and the patient grows weaker, the treatment changes and the price goes up. The sorcerer will begin a series of bird or animal sacrifices, the first and least expensive of which may be a chicken. To the accompaniment of appropriate incantations, the blood is sprinkled on the floor and herbs and poultices are given the patient while everyone waits to see what happens. If the patient continues to get worse and the family can afford the price, the next sacrifice may be a pig. The ultimate sacrifice, which comes only when the illness is very serious, is a water buffalo.

The central highlanders believe that the gods are pleased when the intestines of any animal are used in the proper manner. In the case of water buffalo, the proper usage is twining the intestines about the branches of a living tree. The bark is skinned off young saplings near the chief's house. Since this treatment stunts their growth, every village has a number of small live trees used as prayer poles. Instead of rising to twenty-five or thirty feet, the trees stop growing at about twelve feet. The branches bend at the top and wave in the breeze about the chief's house, like the arms of the spirit that is being worshiped. On the bare branches are placed woodcarvings of small birds, which themselves have sacred meanings to the villagers. When a water buffalo's intestines are entwined about a prayer pole, it means somebody is very sick and the gods are being asked to make him well.

This is what was done for the boy with the abscess. His parents had paid the sorcerer more than six thousand piastres, about $60 United States, which represented more than half their annual income. The boy would have died if he had not been given proper medical care. His mother was sent to us by a Wycliffe Bible translator named Janice Saul, who always did what she could to get the sick of Nam San and surrounding communities to come to us rather than go to their sorcerers. Nam San is a polyglot village made up of North Vietnamese refugees. Janice, who had watched this boy continue to deteriorate, had spent two weeks pleading with the mother to take him to DaMpao. Only when the ultimate treatment of water buffalo intestines on a prayer pole had no effect did she comply.

I had to handle the village sorcerers with great care so they wouldn't be resentful if I succeeded where they had failed. On my next visit to Nam San I asked Janice to take me to the sorcerer who had tried to cure the little boy's abscess, but she couldn't find him.

"Do you think he would be willing to talk to me about his work some time?" I asked.

"I think he'd be flattered," she said. "He was really very much impressed."

On a subsequent visit to Nam San, Janice asked me if we had room for another V.M.O. student.

"Not right now," I said. "But I'd be glad to take him into our next class. Who is he?"

"The sorcerer," she said.

One afternoon I saw a man with a spinal-cord tumor in the Koho village of Dahuyen. The sorcerer there had been treating him for weeks, but the patient continued to get progressively worse. Before giving him any medication, I went to the sorcerer and said through an interpreter, "I'm

176

sure what you are doing must be very good, and I'd like to learn more about it."

"But I don't seem to be able to make this man well," he said.

"What have you done?" I asked.

I listened while he outlined the usual course of village sorcery—the sacrifice of a chicken first, then of a pig, then of a water buffalo, the draping of the water buffalo's intestines around the branches of a living tree near the chief's house, the application of herbs and poultices, the prayers, and the incantations.

When he had finished, I said, "I have some things here that may make your medicine even stronger. If you and I work together, perhaps the patient will get well faster. Then you will be a more respected man in the village and I will be a better doctor for knowing some of the things that make you a good sorcerer."

"The man is not much better," the sorcerer said. "He needs stronger medicine. If you have any, I think you should give it to him."

By making him feel we were working together to cure the patient, I got cooperation instead of animosity. From then on the sorcerer always met us on our village visits to Dahuyen. Whenever we had a patient with whom he had worked, we talked seriously about his treatment and then agreed to try mine.

This attitude works in some villages and doesn't in others. It all depends upon the sorcerer. Older sorcerers are less inclined to accept us because they have been practicing a long time and don't want to change. Besides, they are afraid of losing face and their position in the community. Young sorcerers, on the other hand, are willing to learn and are pleased when we accept them as friends and fellow workers. We hope more will eventually come to us as students and return to their villages with what little practical knowledge of medicine we can teach them in a few months.

It is as important to get the chief's cooperation as the sorcerer's. At Rien Boling, just beyond Loverly Valley about five kilometers east of us, the chief, a hypochondriac with a weakness for heavy rice wine, always insisted on being the first in line at our clinic. One afternoon, when I drove there with Frank, Ann, and K'Mui, our V.M.O. student from Rien Boling, we had a typical visit. Inside the village gates we passed putrefied water buffalo intestines swaying in the light breeze on sapling branches near the chief's house, which led me to believe someone might be pretty sick. As usual, the chief was our first patient.

"Does anyone need emergency help?" I asked K'Mui.

He looked down the line of patients, mostly mothers with runny-nosed children, and shook his head.

"Does the chief?" I said.

"He's drunk again," Frank murmured as we unloaded our boxes of medicine and instruments.

I turned to K'Mui and said, "If you see the sorcerer, ask him whom the water buffalo intestines are for."

When we were ready to begin the clinic, the chief, staggering a little, moved up to the chair in front of me, sat on it, and held out his arm.

"Welcome to our village, Bac-Si," he said.

"Thank you," I said, strapping a blood-pressure cuff just above his elbow. I squeezed the bulb, watched the needle as it moved along the indicator, and said, "The good chief of this important village is in excellent health."

He grinned when K'Mui translated, but refused to leave the chair, holding up the whole line. I asked K'Mui to find out why he wouldn't move.

"He wants medicine," K'Mui said.

I took the chief's arm, swabbed it, and injected multi-B vitamins, which would do no harm and might help sober him up a little. Only after he had the shot would he stand up and make room for a bare-breasted mother with a one-year-old daughter in a sling on her left side. The baby's nose was streaming and her breathing labored. K'Mui took the rectal temperature and together we listened to lungs filled with the coarse noise of bronchitis. After explaining to K'Mui the difference between that and the sticky crepitant sounds of pneumonia, I lifted the child to my lap to feel the abdomen for signs of an enlarged spleen or possible tumors.

The baby cooed, and I felt a warm wetness on my thigh. When I quickly held her aloft she began squalling, while her mother blushed and the chief roared with laughter. After a look at Frank and Ann sputtering, I broke up myself, then the whole clinic exploded. The chief stepped up, his smile warm and genuine through the haze of his intoxication, laid a hand on my shoulder, and walked away. It was his way of showing that he and his people accepted me completely.

Later, just before we left for DaMpao, K'Mui said, "I saw the sorcerer, Bac-Si."

"What did he say?"

"The water buffalo intestines on the living tree were for the chief."

After supper that night I talked to some of the V.M.O. students on the front porch of the main building. The only sounds in the evening quiet were the gentle rustling of trees in the summer breeze and the distant clatter of Monsieur Tom and his crew cleaning up in the kitchen. Despite an occasional shot off in the mountains, there was an atmosphere of warmth and good will and peace, enhanced by the light of the rising moon.

"Who is the most important person in the world?" I asked.

The students looked uncertainly at each other and at me, then Miss Mai, our newest Vietnamese class member, hesitantly replied, "Bac-Si?"

179

"No, Miss Mai. Not Bac-Si. Not the doctors or the nurses or the lab technicians."

"The sorcerers?" ventured a new arrival from a Koho village.

"No. Not the sorcerers."

"President Johnson?" asked H'Klas, back for the weekend from school in DaLat.

"No, H'Klas," I said. "Not President Johnson." I looked at him and said, "You are." Then, to Miss Mai and to each of the others on the porch, I said, "You are—and you—and you—and you. To yourselves, each of you is the most important person in the world."

They sat in silence, then K'Moung spoke. "Bac-Si," he said, "I have suspected there is something inside me that is"—he faltered, groping for the right word—"special."

He paused, and added, "As a boy I can remember listening at night from my bed to the music and chanting of my elders, to the praying of the sorcerers, to all the sounds of the village. And it would come to me that my mind, my heart, my life could mean something."

That started a discussion among the students, Koho and Vietnamese, about life and what it meant. Each had an opinion to express, a story to tell, an incident to recall. These people swapped their ideas in soft voices and stopped only when the moon was high in the sky. I didn't say another word, for I had nothing constructive to add, but I stayed until the talk was over. Only as I began walking slowly to my quarters did I realize how far these young people had come from the recent loincloth-and-crossbow era of their own fathers and the spirit worshiping and sorcery of their own contemporaries.

CHAPTER

18

Lieutenant Dale Myercourt, United States Navy skipper of an armed junk in the Mekong Delta, stopped by for a visit at DaMpao one day. While we talked, a Special Forces sergeant just back from DaNang dropped in, and Dale asked how things were going.

"We had sort of a disconcerting experience last week," the sergeant said. "We liberated a village of seven hundred people south of DaNang, and then found they didn't like being liberated."

Dale, who had been leaning back in his chair with his feet on a table, sat up straight.

"How come?" he said.

The sergeant shook his head. "This was a Vietnamese town which the Viet Cong had taken nine months before. We went back in there as advisors with a force of South Vietnamese Rangers, and cleared the Viet Cong out. We thought sure everyone would be delighted."

He paused, lit a cigarette, and said, "No reason they shouldn't be. After all, they were supposed to be captives of an enemy force. We had a terrible time retaking the place. It was so strongly defended by Viet Cong regulars and well-trained local militia that both sides suffered heavy losses. We had them outnumbered, though, and the Viet Cong slipped out during the night. We could tell almost exactly when, because the shooting stopped. We waited until morning, then walked in unopposed."

The sergeant, peering at Dale, took a deep drag of his cigarette, let the smoke drift out through his mouth and nose, and said, "We had been told it was one of the filthiest, sickest villages in the whole province."

"Was it?" Dale asked.

"Maybe it once had been."

"What did you find?"

"Women, children, old men," the sergeant said. "And a new school, a freshly dug pit privy, a new well, a meeting hall—and an abandoned medical clinic."

"A medical clinic?" I said.

"Yup. Set up by the Viet Cong. Whoever was running it skipped out along with everybody else. Funny thing," the sergeant went on, "that was the only village I went into that didn't have human feces all over the compound. The Viet Cong had cleaned it up, started a school, provided pure drinking water, even got a medic to see patients regularly."

"And you broke it up," I said.

The sergeant nodded. "We broke it up," he said.

"No wonder they didn't fall all over you, Sergeant," Dale said. "We've seen similar things in the Delta. In some places the Viet Cong are losing the war and winning the people."

"Which really means they're winning the war," the sergeant said. "I know of Koho and Rahde tribal villages where the Viet Cong have married into Montagnard families just to create political influence. It's working. They know what the people want, and they give it to them."

When the boys rose to leave, I shook hands with each and said, "Isn't it strange that some of the Viet Cong who deny the importance of individual human rights set up a program that seems to give it highest priority? And our side, preaching the great worth of each human being, seems to be building a program that is impersonal and at times utterly indifferent."

It was true. The Viet Cong lived among the people and, in the case of the sergeant's village near DaNang, actually made improvements. In the whole of Tuyen Duc province I knew of only one American official spending

182

all his time with the people, and he lived at DaMpao with us.

I never saw Dale Myercourt again. He was killed aboard his junk several months later. I don't know what happened to the sergeant. The day he dropped by was the only time I met him, and I never knew his name. I hope he got home safely, and that he was able to get his message across to people who might do something about it.

The work of the Viet Cong in the village the sergeant had described to Dale and me that night in DaMpao was more the exception than the rule, but it did point up one of our biggest problems in South Vietnam—we of the West simply didn't (and don't) know enough about a people whose freedom we're trying to preserve. Even a man such as Father Vallencort, who had worked closely among the Montagnards for more than sixteen years, could make an occasional mistake.

Father Villencort, a French-Canadian Dominican priest, organized a school in DaNung, a Koho hamlet a thousand yards north of us. Until the Special Forces medics came along, he was the nearest thing to a Western doctor the Montagnards had. Although he knew little about medicine, he had a French-English edition of Dr. Jack Lange's handbook, in which he looked up symptoms, treating sick people as directed. He brings his patients to us now, attends our V.M.O. graduations, and is a good friend of Project Concern.

With all his experience in Montagnard country, Father Vallencort, with the best of intentions, built a football-sized playground with soccer goals at each end for the Koho children, hoping it would draw more to his school. The first day the kids used it, they ran up and down for about five minutes, then dropped from exhaustion. What Father Vallencort forgot was that the Koho children, practically starving, lacked the strength to use the playground. Today it's overgrown with weeds and the soccer goals are rotting away.

The people of Southeast Asia need more than equipment such as playgrounds, schools, hospitals, and toilets. When British authorities first built hospitals in Hong Kong they wondered why the sick Chinese didn't take advantage of them. Schools are useless if nobody attends. And toilets are a waste of time if nobody uses them. We learned that when we first showed villagers how to build them, then failed to return for a few weeks. When we finally did, we found sanitary conditions no better than they had been before because the people ignored the toilets. They began using them only when we sent V.M.O.'s back to the villages, not only to teach the people, but to keep after them until they understood. The British got the sick Hong Kong Chinese into their hospital only by going after them and keeping after them. Father Vallencort got kids into his school only by going among them day after day, until he had convinced them and their parents he was their friend. He told me his playground was a monument to good intentions gone wrong. Had he realized the effect of a starvation diet on children, he never would have built it.

But he has the right idea. The only way to help poverty-stricken people is to work and live among them. There is no substitute for personal support, the kind of support the Viet Cong gave the villagers up near DaNang which, incidentally, is one of the few decent Viet Cong gestures I've ever heard of. The Viet Cong around DaMpao terrorized most villages, tearing down fences, setting fires, intimidating Vietnamese and Kohos alike with threats and wild rumors. A touch of real friendship, a good deal of close personal attention, the sight of flesh-and-blood assistance can more than offset any gains made by the Viet Cong anywhere in South Vietnam. Food, theory, equipment mean nothing without people to back them up. And neither, of course, do arms.

A combination of hatred of the Viet Cong, dissatisfaction with the South Vietnamese, and suspicion of the Americans has spawned a strange military unit in the central highlands which operates independently of everyone. These troops are made of Montagnard fighting men mostly from the Koho and Rahde tribes, whose numerical strength is so little known that I have heard estimates ranging all the way from 2,500 to 10,000. Loyal only to a Rahde colonel and based in Cambodia near the South Vietnamese border, this is a well-organized, well-armed, well-trained regiment of fighting men dedicated to restoring peace and stability to their country. The Montagnards call them the "Same-Same"; others refer to them as the "Soldiers in White" or the "Third Force." They make stabbing raids here and there, mostly in villages occupied by the Viet Cong, who fear them as much as Americans. Wearing white, sometimes traveling on horseback, they are South Vietnam's knights in shining armor, a mysterious company of resourceful soldiers who trust nobody but their own people.

K'Moung and H'Klas both have told me that the Third Force is significant in our security at DaMpao. These soldiers know of us and our interest in the Kohos. They are so impressed with the work we do and so anxious that nothing happen to us that they are ready to fight for our protection, according to K'Moung and H'Klas. All our Koho V.M.O.'s know members of the Third Force. I even have reason to believe some of these soldiers and their families have been at our clinics and perhaps even spent nights in our hospital. But they operate so secretly that none has ever been directly identified to me. The nearest village to us they ever raided was Filion, where, dressed in their white outfits and on horseback, they literally rode off some unwelcome Viet Cong who had tried to use the place as an overnight sanctuary.

This guerrilla organization, regardless of its size, is an important military factor in the central highlands. There is no chance of the Viet Cong winning these men over, but our forces should be able to find a way. The "Soldiers in White" neither like nor dislike Americans; they just don't know what to make of them. Although Project Concern is an international medical charitable organization, I'm sure the men of the Third Force know many of us are Americans, yet they still feel somewhat responsible for our safety. And I'm sure if they had to make a choice between the Viet Cong and the United States, they'd take the United States. Nothing would be more helpful in the central highlands campaign than to win them over. It hasn't yet been done at this writing, but it should be and it can be.

One day just before our first V.M.O. class graduated, I asked Major Digger Moravek why we couldn't go farther afield for our village clinics. Up to that point we had confined them to a radius of about fifteen miles from DaMpao. There were dozens of villages beyond it that could use our help.

"It depends on where you go, Jim," Digger said. "I don't want you wandering into some strange place, willy-nilly, because you never know when you'll walk into a Viet Cong nest. Besides, the farther away you go, the longer it will take to get back, and you must not travel after dark."

"What about Psourr?" I said. "We've got a V.M.O. student, K'Chai, who comes from there. He wants to go back after he graduates, and we've never been there."

"Psourr is twenty miles away over rough roads. It would take you an hour and a half each way."

"We could leave early in the afternoon."

Digger shrugged. "Too far for you to go alone," he said. "Tell you what. I'll come around next Friday with four men and lead you there in our jeep. Don't go without us."

My conscience began bothering me. After all, these men were American troops. I didn't want Digger risking himself or them for us.

"Don't make a special trip," I said. "Pick a day when you'll be going to Psourr anyway."

"We have to stop in a lot of places for security checks," Digger said. "This won't interfere with our schedule. We'll get over here around noon."

I told K'Chai we would take him to Psourr Friday, and he looked forward to the trip all week. Friday morning I had an emergency call from the Missionary Alliance School in DaLat and I didn't get back to DaMpao until well after twelve. K'Chai, his handsome green eyes glistening, his face wreathed in a huge smile, met me at the gate. He had obviously been waiting anxiously for me.

"We go to Psourr, Bac-Si?" he said.

I wondered about Digger, then decided he must already have been at DaMpao and gone. He said he had other stops to make, so he would probably be waiting for us at Psourr. I decided it would surely be all right for us to go there.

"Yes, Mr. K'Chai," I said. "Just give me time to change."

I went to my quarters, got into blue jeans and heavy boots in case I had to get out and push the Mollie T. if it got stuck in the mud, picked up Bertha, H'Doy, and K'Chai, and started out. With the wet season still on, the road was terrible. After a while all I could see were woods and tremendous puddles, with patches of ruts here and there marking a route that only K'Chai knew. He must have got us to Psourr by radar, for I was hopelessly lost long before we were anywhere near the place. Unable to go more than twelve or fifteen miles an hour, constantly afraid we'd get stuck, always wondering if K'Chai really knew where he was leading us, I jounced painfully along, my only consolation my assurance that Digger and his men would be waiting at Psourr to lead us back. Finally, we made a last splashing turn, and reached the gates of the village, where ten or fifteen people, attracted by the noise of our motor, were waiting for us.

They all yelled happily when K'Chai, clad in his white

Project Concern medical jacket, jumped from the Mollie T. By the time Bertha, H'Doy, and I climbed out, K'Chai had brought the chief over to meet us. He bowed and, with K'Chai interpreting, said, "Bac-Si, we are so pleased that you honor our village with your presence."

"Thank you," I said. "It is an honor to be here."

"And we are glad you have taken Mr. K'Chai and given him medical training."

"He is an excellent student."

"We look forward to the day when Mr. K'Chai can come to treat our people."

"It will be soon," I said.

Where was Digger?

He couldn't have been in the village. It wasn't big enough to hide a jeep and five or six American soldiers. Besides, he would have been the first to greet us.

"Where is Major Moravek?" I asked the chief.

"We haven't seen him."

I told K'Chai to describe the jeep and to tell the chief Digger was supposed to meet us. The chief shook his head and said no jeep had been out that way in months. I looked at my watch. It was three-thirty, almost too late to start a clinic, considering the condition of the roads and the length of time it could take to get back to DaMpao. Without Digger's protection, we might be asking for trouble if we stayed. But K'Chai and H'Doy were already setting up our medical equipment and sick villagers were getting into line. Perhaps an hour of clinic, I thought, would be all right. We could leave at four-thirty and still get back before nightfall.

In that hour we saw forty patients, some of whom belonged in the hospital. "These people will die if they don't come to us soon," I told K'Chai.

"They will come, Bac-Si," he said. "The chief will see that they come."

We said good-by and left. With Digger still missing, I

was more nervous about the trip than Bertha or the students. Nothing bothered her, and the boys showed no signs of apprehension. All I could think of was that dreadful road back and the possibilities of getting stuck on it. The last thing I wanted was to spend a night in the jungle on the fringe of Viet Cong territory ten or fifteen miles from home.

With K'Chai pointing the way and me blindly following his directions, we bumped and splashed along for half an hour with nothing worse than a couple of scares when the wheels spun and the Mollie T. wouldn't move. Both times Bertha took the wheel while the students and I got out and pushed, and we worked the car free. But the third time we got into a gummy goo that mired us deeper with every turn. We took some logs from the woods and lined them up with the wheels, but succeeded only in burying the logs. We rocked the car, but succeeded only in splattering ourselves with mud. We pushed while Bertha maneuvered gears and accelerator, but succeeded only in exhausting ourselves. At times I was in mud so deep it went over the tops of my boots and down inside them, soaking my socks and pants and making every step a squishy mess. We were stuck—good and stuck.

"Listen," Bertha said.

We stopped slopping around in the muck and cocked our ears. Sure enough, we heard the sound of a car off in the distance, then closer and closer.

"Sounds like a jeep," Bertha said.

"Digger, maybe?" I said.

"Must be. Who else could be on this road at this time of day?"

Maybe the Viet Cong, but Bertha was an optimist and that would never occur to her. All we could do was wait until the car came into view. K'Chai and H'Doy leaned against the Mollie T. on the side nearest the jungle. Bertha, a slight smile on her face, remained calmly at the wheel,

189

looking exactly as if she were waiting for a traffic light to change at a busy intersection in San Mateo. I wiped my brow, while murmuring a little prayer that Major Digger Moravek would be driving that jeep.

The noise of the motor grew louder, then suddenly the car appeared. Digger wasn't driving, but I recognized him by the ever-present pipe sticking out of his mouth.

"It's the Major," I said.

The boys straightened up and walked around to the front of the Mollie T. Bertha didn't move, but her smile was broad now. I heaved a huge sigh of thankful relief.

When the jeep pulled up to us, Digger called, "Jim, for heaven's sake, what are you doing here?"

"I thought you'd be at Psourr," I said.

The jeep stopped, two soldiers jumped out with their carbines at the ready, and two more began unloading chains and hooks to pull us out. The boys with the guns faced the jungle, looking as if they meant business. I nodded toward them and said, "Digger, is it that bad?"

"The area's crawling with Viet Cong," he said. "They're all over the place."

"Oh, my," I said. "I'm afraid we caused you trouble. I got back from DaLat so late I thought you had been at DaMpao and gone over in this direction."

"No trouble," Digger said. "We're just glad we caught up with you. We were later than you getting to DaMpao, and figured this was the only place you would have gone. Jim—"

"Yes?"

"Do me a favor?"

"Sure."

"Next time, wait for us."

"Yes, *sir*, Major," I said.

CHAPTER

19

I met Lieutenant Jim Wilkie for the first time when he literally dropped in from the sky. Pilot of an HUI-B helicopter, he was a cheerful, friendly young man with an almost perpetual smile on his face. He came down one afternoon, after circling overhead for several minutes to make sure there weren't any Viet Cong within easy firing distance. The chopper had a made-to-order pad next to our compound, which had been built by the Special Forces who occupied DaMpao before we moved in.

After shaking hands, Jim said, "Doc, I hear you can use our kind of transportation."

"Bless Digger Moravek," I thought. He must have told Jim about our trip to Psourr.

"Use it?" I said. "Believe me, you're like manna from heaven. There are a million places we ought to go to and can't reach in the Land-Rover."

Jim turned toward his chopper and bowed. "Be my guest," he said. "Wednesdays all right?"

"Any day is all right."

"Okay. If some higher priority job keeps us from making it, we'll let you know."

"Wonderful," I said. "I'll dope out a weekly itinerary. Gee, this is great. We can make three or four villages in one afternoon in that thing."

Jim and his crew of two waist gunners, Sergeants Donaldson and Ramos, came around the following Wednesday and, with a few exceptions, almost every Wednesday thereafter. We planned three or four basic trips, so the gaps between visits wouldn't be too long. One trip into a village was little better than none. People forgot the virtues of proper sanitation unless the rules were frequently repeated

191

and demonstrated. Besides, every village had its share of continuing cases requiring long-term treatment and examination.

Just after twelve one Wednesday we heard the swishing of Jim Wilkie's "Huey." By the time it was on the pad, its main rotor kicking up weeds and dust with its slow, noisy spinning, Ann Kidder, Miss K'Mum, K'Crah, and H'Klas were standing with me waiting to climb aboard. After the two sergeants had helped load our medical gear under the seats and strapped us in with wide, webbed belts, one of the boys got me into a radio headset and I heard Jim say, "Where today, Doc?"

"Kamboutte, just east over the river from Tung Nhia," I said, pointing to the spot on a map he held up. "Then Filion, Tournoum, and Huat Cam Le." The latter was near DaMpao, but we hadn't been there in weeks.

I grinned when I mentioned Tournoum, for it evoked memories of my first tortuous trip there, when H'Klas and I had driven down the winding cliffside beyond DaLat soon after my arrival at DaMpao. It was an insane venture which I would never repeat in the Mollie T., but a pleasure in a chopper. That first experience seemed years ago, for K'Chong, the young husband who had returned to the hospital with us and his sick wife, was now our V.M.O. there.

Jim Wilkie twisted the throttle handle to increase the speed and pitch of the main rotor and the chopper tottered momentarily, then moved off the pad in a circular cloud of red dust. We went straight up, hovered over the compound, and headed east, past one village after another. H'Klas, on his first helicopter ride, recognized one of the little compounds as DaMe, his home.

In ten minutes we covered forty kilometers of hills, bridges, villages, and rivers, a trip that would have taken the Mollie T. six hours. Kamboutte was actually three closely-knit villages huddled together in an odd cluster which we called Kamboutte A, Kamboutte B, and Kamboutte C.

Each was ringed by a trench and rows of arrow-sharp bamboo spikes that angled upward and forward. There were more Viet Cong around the Kambouttes than Da-Mpao, and they were more active. We made one pass high over the villages, then circled down around their edges, minimizing the danger of ground fire from any lurking enemy patrols.

We settled in a fog of weeds and dust, while scores of excited Kohos poured out of a small gate to meet us. As a sergeant who had never traveled with us before helped Ann down the two-foot step to the ground, he said, "You're not going in there, are you? They may be hiding Viet Cong."

"I'm going in," she said. "We've been here before. One of our V.M.O.'s is here. These people are our friends."

The sergeant looked at Jim Wilkie, who nodded. After our gear was unloaded, the chopper took off. It would be back for us in an hour.

K'Duk, in his white Project Concern jacket with blue lettering, was waiting for us. As we shook hands, I said, "It's good to be in your village, Mr. K'Duk. Any trouble?"

"No trouble, Bac-Si. No Viet Cong come here."

He led the way through a double gate to our clinic facility, which was in the village community house.

"We have best defense against Viet Cong," he said. "We are poor. Nothing here for Viet Cong to take." He smiled, and said, "Today is a village holiday. One of our boys becomes a man. After clinic, you are all to be chief's guests at our small ceremony."

It would cut short our clinic, but that was secondary. These proud, sensitive people would be insulted if we ignored their ceremony or failed to allow time for it. We accepted their rites and superstitions in the same spirit with which we accepted their sorcerers. I always found one of their beliefs especially interesting. Many Kohos thought all rivers run to a common end, a great hole in the ground. In some villages people are assigned to guard the hole to keep it from becoming clogged. If it gets stopped up, the floods come.

As we prepared for the clinic, K'Duk answered my questions about sanitation in the villages.

"Pit privies?" I said.

"Dug and being used."

"Drinking water?"

"Boiled."

"Insect control?"

"Good."

"Bathing?"

He shrugged, sheepishly grinning. Everywhere we went, bathing was a problem. With no showers, people either used nearby rivers, which were often contaminated, or didn't bathe at all. In general, the Kambouttes were in pretty good shape, however. K'Duk had seen to that.

The clinic began. An old man in great pain from loose, badly infected teeth needed immediate attention. We gave him a local anesthetic, pulled out what teeth he had left, swabbed his gums, and told K'Duk to swab them daily until they were healed. We rechecked several outpatient tuberculosis cases whom K'Duk treated regularly, all of whom showed improvement. We had some deeply infected wounds to dress, and one man with a broken arm to check. Through K'Duk, he asked if he might continue wearing his sling, of which he was very proud. When we told him he would need it for two or three more weeks, he walked away with a huge grin on his face.

Ann and Miss K'Mum were handing out birth-control items, along with careful instructions on how to use them, when a severely undernourished man with ulcers on both feet was carried in by his family. The villagers shrank back, for he was a leper. It was against regulations, but we hoped the chopper crew would let us take him back to DaMpao where we could treat him properly. Just as we finished making him comfortable on a stretcher, K'Duk tugged at my arm to let me know it was time for the ceremony celebrating the boy's conversion to manhood.

Outside, the village elders sat around several porcelain pots, each filled to the brim with a watery rice wine called *nam pei*, and each equipped with a long reed straw that poked out more than a foot. *Nam pei* is so heady that only a few sips will affect anyone not used to it. Since I'm not a drinker and had more clinics that day, I had to be particularly careful, yet I couldn't refuse. I sat beside the chief around the largest pot. A very old, deeply crinkled Koho woman who did not drink sat among the elders, apparently measuring the amount each took. When one finished, she carefully refilled the pot to its original level. She didn't have much to add after I had sipped. I had ambivalent feelings about that drink. I didn't want it to be too strong, yet hoped there was enough alcohol to kill the bacteria that must have been crawling around the straw tip I took into my mouth. Even though I drank very little, the people, especially the grinning chief, seemed pleased.

Just as the straw began to make the rounds for a second time, I heard the welcome drone of chopper rotors. Jim Wilkie began coming down in tight circles and the ceremony was forgotten for the moment while everyone turned to watch. The chief rose, the others followed, and I scrambled to my feet, delighted not to have to take another sip of that deadly *nam pei*.

When Jim agreed to take the leper, we carefully made him comfortable in a corner of the chopper and started for Filion, our next stop. Miss K'Mum and Ann got out with me while K'Crah went on to DaMpao with the sick man. The rest of the day was uneventful. We ran short clinics in Filion, Tournoum, and Huat Cam Le, and were home long before dark. I thanked Jim and his crew, shook hands all around, nodded agreement when they said they

195

would see me the following Wednesday, and stepped to the ground.

Frank and Junior Duong, Guy Brehon's assistant, met me in the Mollie T.

"There's an emergency at the hospital, Jim," Frank said. "I thought we'd better drive you up. A small boy has been hit by a hand grenade."

In the ward, a frightened four-year-old Vietnamese boy sat against the thin gray metal frame at the head of a cot, holding tightly to his father's hand while K'Moung stood by.

"Bac-Si," K'Moung said, "a phosphate grenade exploded near Thong Binh this morning. Several children were burned, this boy the worst."

The child's face was severely swollen, his skin splattered with tiny deep black holes, but what worried me was the condition of his eyes. Both were completely closed by the puffy skin around the lids, and when I opened them I saw that both corneas had been burned. I wished desperately that we had an ophthalmologist in the compound, but there probably wasn't one in the whole of South Vietnam. The boy might need a transplant, but I didn't know where to get a fresh, frozen cornea nor was I equipped to perform such a delicately technical operation. All we could do was take emergency measures and hope for the best.

"K'Moung," I said, "let's apply cortisone ointment to the eyes, dress his burns with Furacin, get him on oral penicillin, and sedate him." While K'Crah, who had followed me into the ward, looked over my shoulder, I wrote the prescriptions as I talked. He took them, hurried to the pharmacy, and was back with everything I requested before I had completed a thorough examination of the youngster. Except for the eyes, his wounds, while painful, were not serious.

Through K'Moung I told the father there was a chance the boy might be blinded, a particular tragedy in South

Vietnam where there is no welfare, no special consideration for the visually handicapped and, as far as I knew, no school for the blind. The father sighed, and K'Moung patted him on the shoulder. The boy, a warm, friendly youngster, swiftly became a staff favorite. Lynn Allen gave him a toy dog, which he took everywhere with him. He wandered around the ward, making friends with the other patients and smiling despite the bandages we kept over his eyes. We took them off only to apply medication.

On the fourth day he gave an excited whoop, grinning and pointing to show that he could see when we removed his bandages. We continued to treat him for two more days until we were sure his vision had not been seriously impaired. At the end of the week he was ready to go home, with nothing worse than a few scars to show for his ordeal. His father gave us a chicken and a million dollars' worth of tearful thank-yous. The last we saw of them, they were walking jauntily out of the hospital hand in hand, the boy clutching his toy dog in his free arm.

That night we had a happy, relaxed, fun-filled English class, with more laughs than usual. We followed a published text put out by the Vietnamese-American Association. The evening lesson was in introductions and invitations into one's home, which we decided to act out, with hilarious results. In broken English Koho V.M.O.'s invited their Vietnamese counterparts, who accepted in English fully as fractured.

In a typical exchange, a Koho would say, "Sit down. Tea please. Come in. Won't you?" And a Vietnamese would reply, "No. I will. Thank you." All this was complicated by my own failure to remember the meaning of head signals in South Vietnam. Ordinarily, when you move your head up and down you mean "yes," and when you shake it from side to side you mean "no." Since it's exactly the opposite there, I continually signaled yes when I meant no'and vice versa.

Just as the class broke up there were three shots followed by a short burst of automatic fire from the direction of the hospital. When we had practice alerts, we called them with a two-shot warning. This was the real thing. The lights went out and students, cooks, soldiers, mechanics and medical staff rushed through the light of a half-moon to assigned positions. I hadn't been in my fox hole five minutes before K'Moung and H'Klas, more relaxed than I had ever seen them during an alert, quietly approached me.

"It is not Viet Cong," H'Klas said. "It is Same-Same."

"Third Force?" I whispered.

"Our friends," K'Moung said. "If they come, they will not hurt us. They are Koho, the same as we."

"If they try to take our medicine or food, will you fight them?" I said.

"They will not hurt us or take our supplies," he said. "They will protect us. Viet Cong nearby, and Same-Same don't want anything to happen to us."

The alert ended at midnight. Whoever had fired the shots must have been on our side—either our own guards or those mysterious "Soldiers in White." But it hadn't been a false alarm. The Viet Cong had attacked Huat Cam Le, killing seven villagers and wounding several more, according to a report Larry Wiesner relayed to me. I wanted to go over there, but we had strict orders not to travel in the Land-Rover unescorted after an alert. I was about reconciled to sticking close to DaMpao when we had an unheralded visit from Jim Wilkie in his chopper.

"Just want to make sure you folks are all right," he yelled over the noise of his big rotor.

"We're fine, but we're worried about Huat Cam Le," I said. "Would you mind taking us over there? I think they need us."

"Get your crew and gear, and come aboard," he said. I rounded up Ann, K'Crah, and K'Nhum, our V.M.O.

student from Huat Cam Le, got some supplies together, and we took off. Huat Cam Le actually was so close it was just a matter of climbing and descending almost in a straight line in a chopper. The trip would have taken an hour by car, for the village was isolated by dense woods and the only way to reach it was over a rough, deeply rutted track, an ordeal in the Mollie T.

The Viet Cong had not only raided the tiny hamlet, but before leaving had machine-gunned some women and children in the trench around the perimeter. The dead had already been buried in the jungle by the time we arrived. The terrified villagers hid from us until K'Nhum stepped out of the chopper. Only when they recognized him would they lead us to the huts where the wounded lived.

Back in camp, we were greeted with an angry rumor that Huat Cam Le had been hit by South Vietnamese troops, not Viet Cong. Some of the V.M.O.'s were so resentful that they sullenly talked of leaving, especially after they managed to transform rumors into what they called "near knowledge." Since this was too serious to be ignored, I decided to do something about it at once. Even though it was late afternoon, I insisted that H'Klas, K'-Moung, and H'Doy, whom all the V.M.O.'s admired and trusted, go with me to see Captain Gene Sexton, the American security officer at DaLat. We had to find out once and for all what had really happened at Huat Cam Le. I felt that the danger of driving at dusk was insignificant compared to the danger of the poisonous story sweeping DaMpao. The trip offered minimum risk to only a few of us, the story maximum risk to the entire hospital.

Gene left a dinner party to join us when I explained the problem. As we sat around a table, he looked at the three Montagnards and said, "The Viet Cong attacked Huat Cam Le last night, and then started the rumor that our own people had done it. I spent the whole day checking this with the Vietnamese security officer here in DaLat. We work closely together and understand each other as well as you understand Bac-Si and he you. We went to Huat Cam Le and talked to eyewitnesses. They confirmed the attack and the machine-gunning atrocity."

Even while Gene spoke, we were joined by the Vietnamese security officer, who corroborated everything he told us. H'Klas, K'Moung, and H'Doy, fully satisfied that the vicious story that threatened to tear our compound apart was a lie, told me on the way back to DaMpao that they had never believed it anyhow. Back at the hospital, we held a meeting, at which K'Moung set all the doubters' minds at rest, and there was no more trouble.

But, with the Viet Cong operating all around us, we had to curtail our village visits. At one point we seriously considered pulling back to DaLat until the situation cleared. I gave that up because the outpatient clinic was as heavy as ever, and none of the inpatients wanted to go home. Instead of pulling out, we increased our clinic hours on days when it was inadvisable to leave the hospital compound. There, we were too busy with problems of our own to worry about the Viet Cong.

A young Vietnamese husband came in with his slender, beautiful wife who complained of difficulty in swallowing and in breathing through her mouth. When I depressed the back of her tongue, I noticed a peculiar swelling of the soft palate around the glottis and the uvula. A nasal spectulum showed a new growth almost completely blocking the nasal passage. I wrote a prescription for super-aspirin and said to one of the V.M.O. students helping me, "K'Dong, please take Mrs. Vin into the pharmacy for her medicine."

After they left, I turned to the handsome young husband and said, through K'Moung, "Your wife has cancer in her nose and throat. It has spread so far through her head that she cannot live much longer. I'm sorry."

He stared at me in disbelief while tears rolled down his sun-bronzed face, then spoke to K'Moung, who turned to me and said, "They have been married only a week."

I looked away, partly to give the boy a chance to recover his composure, mostly to keep him from noticing my difficulty in keeping my own. When I looked back, he had steadied himself, stopped weeping, and straightened his shoulders. The last I saw of him, K'Moung was leading him into the treatment room to pick up his bride. She died six weeks later.

A three-year-old boy, his body distended by fluids he could not excrete, was brought in by his father. I suspected nephritis, a common ailment in South Vietnam, where the people, lacking medical facilities, pay no attention to minor infections. Frank's urinalysis confirmed that repeated streptococcus infections had destroyed most of the boy's kidney tissue. The physical findings and the lab tests were so discouraging I knew the case was all but hopeless.

"Your son has badly damaged kidneys," I told the father. "We will give him the best medicine available, but we cannot give him new kidneys. He may not live much longer." I was sick. Routine medical care a year sooner would have saved the boy's life.

One day a four-year-old boy with blue lips that widened into a smile which made my heart flip was carried in by his mother. Despite his age, he could not sit up by himself, let alone walk. With stethoscope and probing fingers I learned that he had probable tetrology of Fallot, a combination of severe congenital heart defects. Much of his blood gushed with each heartbeat from the right to the left, bypassing his lungs and keeping him perpetually short of oxygen. The boy, whose name was Nguyen Van Khanh, could not live without open-heart surgery, which was out of the question at DaMpao.

"Your child has a very bad heart," I told the mother.

In hopes that she would accept the truth rather than the sorcerer's version, which was probably optimistic, I carefully explained what was wrong.

"I understand, Bac-Si," she said, gazing into Khanh's deep-brown eyes. Then she turned and asked, "Have I offended God?"

"No," I said. "You have not offended God. But until Vietnam has a hospital that can treat children like Khanh, God is offended by our indifference."

Khanh's case haunted me. Even surgery might not save him, but I felt he deserved at least that chance. His cheerful grin, his marvelous even disposition, his grateful acceptance of everything we did for him, completely captivated the staff. It seemed criminal that such a fine youngster should simply lie on a hospital bed and waste away when proper surgery might save him.

I wrote Dr. Jack Lange, of the Lange Medical Publications, who is a member of Project Concern's board of directors, outlining the case in detail and asking if he had any suggestions. A few weeks later he sent me a copy of a letter he had received from Dr. Victor Richards of San Francisco's Children's Hospital. In effect, it read, "We are ready to operate if Jim can get the patient over here."

That was the rub ". . . if Jim can get the patient over here." I went to every United States government agency in Saigon, but got nowhere. I asked the military to provide transportation, but that didn't work either. I tried Pan-American Airlines, but they didn't feel they could sponsor the trip. I even requested help from Air Vietnam, but the people there didn't think they could justify the expense. In the end, I asked our own board to pay Khanh's expenses, and that was how we got him to San Francisco.

Dr. Richards operated, and he and a staff made up of the city's finest doctors, assisted by twelve nurses, fought ten days to pull Khanh through. The youngster didn't make it, but at least he had his chance. If we gave every sick Vietnamese as good a chance I think we'd win the people and the war, too.

CHAPTER

20

It would have suited me perfectly if all I had to think about were the diagnosis and treatment of backward, poverty-stricken people with nowhere else to turn. Our first few months at DaMpao were among the happiest of my life for, starting from scratch, we won the confidence of simple villagers who had never known the true meaning of medical care. Our V.M.O. program—we later changed it to V.M.A., for "Village Medical Assistant," since the word "officer" seemed pretentious—was well started. Our people were learning to help themselves in a place where the need for such self-help might suddenly be thrust upon them because of the unsettled conditions of the country. Kohos and Vietnamese were coming to our clinic in increasing numbers. Word of our hospital had spread so widely that patients appeared from as far as a hundred kilometers away. We barely scratched the surface, but we were at least doing that. Fifty Project Concerns couldn't satisfy the needs of the people in South Vietnam.

I was able to concentrate on the medical aspects of my job only for a comparatively short time. Other problems constantly cropped up, first asking, then begging, and finally demanding my attention. Despite the financial help that came to us from the United States, Canada, Australia, New Zealand, and elsewhere, despite the scores of good friends who sent us money every month, despite the enthusiastic and continuing support of Jaycees everywhere, we always seemed to be short of cash. We collected as much as ever, but our expenses doubled soon after we went into South Vietnam. The hospital there was bigger than anything we had in Hong Kong, even the *Yuah Oi* and the *Ming Ling* combined. The boat clinic, the Walled City, Jordan Valley, and a fourth Hong Kong clinic we added in 1966 in the fishing village of Lei Yue Mun cost no more than the DaMpao complex alone. Our current budget calls for expenditures of $7,000 a month in Hong Kong and $7,000 a month in South Vietnam. Since it costs $3,000 a month more to operate our headquarters in Coronado, run by Paul Fleener, who is now our executive vice-president, we must raise $17,000 a month to operate efficiently.

We couldn't get by on that except for the scores of volunteers who come to us from all over the world at their own expense and work for nothing on their arrival. Nor could we get by on that except for the economies we are able to effect in Hong Kong. We established the Lei Yue Mun clinic, for example, at no extra expense in medical staff since the team which serves the Walled City in the morning now goes there in the afternoon. We are also fortunate in having so many competent refugees from Red China available in Hong Kong. Worth far more than we pay them, they work for a subsistence wage and the satisfaction of helping in a great cause. We should pay them more, but we can't.

We should pay everybody more. A Project Concern area director gets a base salary of $350 a month if he's married, $250 if not. A lab technician in Hong Kong is paid $200 a month, half that in South Vietnam, where we provide housing. The same is true of nurses. These people are really volunteers, for the salaries we pay them are little more than tokens.

While our drug requirements are far beyond what we get from the sample-drug program, we actually have to buy only about 10 per cent of what we use. The rest is donated from one source or another. Project Handclasp transports our supplies, but except when we can travel with one of the armed services on a space-available basis our personal transportation costs are tremendous. We include promotion expenses—another large item—in the operation of our Coronado office, where Paul and two secretaries work for what they need rather than what they are worth, with the assistance of many volunteers. Our family finances are controlled by a strictly curtailed budget, adequate solely for our own needs and those of our children.

I transform every trip to the States into a fund-raising tour, speaking to anyone who will listen to the story of Project Concern, at the expense of anyone who will pay my way. There was a typical example in March of 1966, when the Freedoms Foundation of Valley Forge, Pennsylvania, honored me with its Freedom Leadership Medal. The Foundation brought me back from South Vietnam and across the country to Philadelphia, where the awards were presented. This enabled me to plan a nation-wide tour of nine cities, resulting in donations we otherwise might not have collected. Mollie, although fundamentally shy and lacking the training in public speaking I received while studying for the ministry, is particularly good at this sort of thing, for she can charm an audience with an appealing combination of looks, brains, and enthusiasm. Project Concern's greatest public-relations asset, she carries our message wherever she can whenever she has the time.

We are not selling a bill of goods, but a hope for the future of the poverty-stricken everywhere. We could have spun a globe with our eyes closed and begun working wherever it stopped, for there is no country in the world, even our own, without its share of the illiterate needy who can use what we try to offer. We began with Tijuana because of its proximity to Coronado, and left only when we knew others would replace us. We went to Hong Kong because it was called to our attention at the time we established Project Concern. We moved into South Vietnam because it is full of little people lost in a big power struggle for control of a country. If conditions permit, we would still like to open a hospital in Cheo Rio. In this Central Highlands province there are 65,000 Jahri tribesmen and 10,000 Vietnamese, all starving and neglected by everyone but sorcerers and a missionary preacher who gives out aspirin and chloroquin for malaria.

We have asked the South Vietnamese government to build the hospital. We would staff it, bring in the drugs and equipment, and provide a Village Medical Assistant training program similar to what we have at DaMpao. We would like to go quickly into Ching Mai in northwestern Thailand, where a million Hill People are without medical care, so that we can establish a hospital before the Red Chinese arrive there. Chou En Lai announced in 1965 that he intended to move his cadres into that very sector. By winning the people with concern and kindness, we could conceivably prevent another Vietnam disaster. We have not given up the idea of going into the Indian state of Orissa, where the only hospital for 14,000,000 hopelessly poor and backward people has but a hundred and fifty beds. We have been asked to go to Peru, one of the neediest nations in the world, with millions of Indians and mestizos living in primitive poverty in almost inaccessible localities. There are so many places to go, so many things to do, so few years to do them in . . .

We have no big objectives—only little ones. We have no desire to send food and medicine and supplies in crates to places we will never see. We don't want to work in provincial capitals or district headquarters cheek by jowl with the leaders of nations and states and provinces and cities. We want to work directly with the people, in or near their villages. We want to integrate ourselves with them, to help them as individuals, to give them the warmth of human contact, to let them know somebody cares, to go into their homes, to know them as individuals and as families and as tribes, not as statistics in an almanac.

Wherever we are, whatever we do, wherever we want to go, however far and wide we hope to spread our services, the most important thing in the world is always the local problem of the moment. Consider our early days at DaMpao, where we had lived a lifetime in a few months in 1964. With the approach of autumn, the wet season was replaced by a dry mountain cold. South Vietnam is a semitropical country, but the central highlands are like highlands everywhere—chilly because they are highlands. It was so cold at the hospital that the families of some of the patients wanted to light fires on the ward floor, which, of course, was out of the question. We gave out all the blankets we had, but that was nowhere nearly enough. People huddled together to keep warm, and wandered around at dawn hollow-eyed from lack of sleep. The cold did what threat of Viet Cong invasion couldn't do—it drove out two inpatients, who left one day without permission.

Perhaps it was the weather, perhaps the sight of tired, discontented people, perhaps the disappearance of the patients, but suddenly everything seemed to be going wrong. The Viet Cong were closing in, always threatening to force us back to DaLat, or to Saigon, or even out of South Vietnam altogether. We faced continual financial crisis, with no way that I could see to cut expenses. Our obligations in Hong Kong had to be met and our obligations at DaMpao were increasing. The political turmoil in South Vietnam generated exasperating red tape resulting in costly delays in the delivery of medicine and supplies. Too much of what we needed was rotting in Saigon, after having been shipped halfway around the world. I kept getting messages from Hong Kong stressing the importance of my presence there.

I was needed in the States for a fund-raising tour, even if we had to pay for it ourselves.

Whenever my morale threatened to sag, I thought of the compensations, of which there were dozens. Our clinic sessions were bigger than ever. Our hospital was full. Our people were working hard, our students learning fast. The war might drive us out of DaMpao someday, but the Kohos and Vietnamese themselves would carry on the program we left behind. Each day was a day gained, a day closer to the time we would not be needed. There were signs of progress wherever I looked. More students than ever were working in the ward, and in the treatment room, and in the pharmacy. Some could do hemoglobins, stool and sputum examinations and urinalyses, and others were learning. It was eminently satisfying to see their eyes light up in newly acquired knowledge when they recognized under a microscope the organisms of tuberculosis, gonorrhea, leprosy, and cholera. These were lessons that would stay with them and be passed on to others long after we left— if we ever had to leave.

I missed Mollie and the children terribly. I wanted to go to Hong Kong just to see them, to touch them, to feel them with me, to let them know they were part of a complete family. If only there were no war in South Vietnam, if only they could live with me in safety, if only we could all be together! My thoughts were so much with them that I knew I had a double ambition in life—to help all the people in the world who needed help, and to be with those I loved. I wanted my wife with me, and my children, as long as they were young. When they grew up, they would go where life took them, but now they needed me and I them.

The ideal situation had been in Hong Kong in the early days of our work there. Then, I had my cake and ate it, too, for my family was with me while I worked among people who needed me. The only trouble was, the longer we were there, the less the people needed me, and I knew now I could never stay in one place as long as I was needed more in another. I would have to settle for a partial family life, seeing my loved ones a few weeks here, a month or two there, for I could not abandon the work I was doing.

I sat alone in our common room one Saturday evening, wrestling with the problem, brooding a little as I prepared to write a nostalgic letter to Mollie. The girls and Frank and Guy and the others had gone to the movies, which I could see flickering in the soft light of a rising half-moon. Off in the distance were the ever-present sounds of the jungle, the squawking of birds, the grunting of boars, the chatter of monkeys, the barking of wild dogs, all punctuated by the periodic sounds of the war, isolated shots that cut through the clear air as though they were yards instead of miles away. Sometimes a voice or a few bars of music drifted up from the movie in the dining hall below. There were noises all around me, but I felt alone—so very much alone.

I heaved a deep sigh, pulled writing paper from a drawer, placed it on the table we used for a desk, and began, "My darling—"

It was a rambling, disjointed letter, so long that I was still writing when the movie ended and the others came back.

"How was the picture?" I asked.

"Nothing special," Frank said.

I looked at my watch, yawned, and folded the partially written letter. The next day was Sunday. I would finish it after church. I would go to Father Vallencort's mass. I would walk over early, then have the common room to myself after hospital rounds.

The mass ended at eight-thirty. I checked the inpatients with K'Moung, walked back to my quarters, and picked up the letter to reread before finishing it. In the harsh light

209

of the morning sun it seemed a pretty poor excuse for a letter. I tore it up, and started over.

"My darling—"

A racing motor gave notice that a car was climbing the hill, and an army jeep pulled up in front of the building. Slightly annoyed at the interruption, I stood up and started slowly for the door, then quickened my pace as I heard my name called in familiar, softly vibrant tones. The next thing I knew Mollie was in my arms.

When we could speak, I said, "What in the world are you doing here?"

"I had to talk to you."

"I'm so glad—so very glad—to see you."

"I couldn't write," Mollie said. "I couldn't wire. I had to *tell* you."

"Tell me what?"

She stepped away from my arms, held my hands in hers, and looked into my eyes.

"Jim, I'm going back to school."

"You're what?"

"I got into Cal Western"—the words tumbled out—"I didn't want to say anything until I was sure. I'm going to take two years of premed."

"Premed?"

"Jim, we can't go on like this indefinitely, with you working and me doing nothing. It will take a long time, but I'm going to be a doctor. Then, wherever you go I'll go, and we can work together."

Mollie completed her premed requirements from Cal Western in 1966. She is now a first-year student at Women's Medical College of Pennsylvania in Philadelphia. In another four years I can have my cake and eat it, too, as I did in Hong Kong. Only this time it won't be just for a year or two. It will be for a whole lifetime.

About the author

Dr. JAMES W. TURPIN was born in the Southern part of this country, educated there and eventually ordained as a Methodist minister. He worked in various parts of the South before setting up his medical practice in Coronado, California, with his wife, Martha, and their four children—three boys and a girl. After establishing Project Concern, Dr. Turpin transferred his activities to Hong Kong and has, for the last several years, divided his time between Hong Kong and Vietnam, where he has set up various hospital facilities for the people of that area. Mrs. Turpin is herself studying to be a doctor, but the Turpins continue to maintain their offices with Project Concern, c/o Postmaster, San Diego, California.

AL HIRSHBERG now divides his time between Boston and Cape Cod and is a columnist for a Boston newspaper, as well as a prolific writer for various publishers. He has most recently written for McGraw-Hill *He Is in Heaven* (1965) and is best known as the co-author of *Fear Strikes Out: The Jimmy Piersall Story*, the biography of the well-known baseball player.